Beef Managem

A practi

By the same author :

The Production and Management of Sheep
Pig Management and Production

Beef Management and Production

A practical guide for farmers and students

Derek H. Goodwin
N.D.A., S.C.D.A., Cert. Ed. (Birmingham)

Lecturer in Animal Husbandry
Gloucestershire College of Agriculture

Hutchinson of London

Hutchinson & Co (Publishers) Ltd
3 Fitzroy Square, London W1 P6JD

London Melbourne Sydney Auckland
Wellington Johannesburg and agencies
throughout the world

First published 1977
© Derek H. Goodwin 1977
Illustrations © Hutchinson 1977

Set in Monotype Imprint
Printed in Great Britain by The Anchor Press Ltd
and bound by Wm Brendon & Son Ltd
both of Tiptree, Essex

ISBN 0 09 127060 X (cased)
ISBN 0 09 127061 8 (paper)

Contents

Acknowledgements

I wish to express my personal thanks to all the people who have assisted me in the research and writing of this book. First, I have drawn freely on the writings of the late John Hammond and his colleagues at Cambridge. The reader should certainly try to study Hammond's *Physiology of Farm Animals* and C. P. McMeekans' *Principles of Livestock*.

I am extremely grateful to W. Simpson, MRCVS, Divisional Veterinary Officer, Gloucestershire Animal Health Department for his invaluable help on the chapters on Health and Disease. To Mr Tom Arnott, the Editor, *Better Breeding*; the Milk Marketing Board for providing the plates of European Breeds of Cattle and for allowing me to use information researched by Mr Philip Tyler of the MMB and published in *Better Breeding*; A. J. Rowlinson of Feed Stock Services (Livestock) Ltd for help with urea feeding; the Meat and Livestock Commission for allowing me to use numerous tables from their publications; the Controller, HMSO, for use of tables from Bulletin 48, *Rations for Livestock*; my colleague Stuart Allan who provided information on grassland utilization; Stuart Freeman who took photographs on stock tasks, and Eirwyn Jenkins for reading parts of the text.

I am particularly grateful to Gordon Cinderby for reading the manuscript and proofs.

I wish to thank Miss Elaine Hopton for her considerable help and guidance in preparing my three books and Kevin McDermott of Hutchinson, for his help and encouragement in writing this manuscript.

Lastly my special thanks to Mrs D. J. Buckland for typing the manuscript.

Derek H. Goodwin
1976

Haven Greatheart   Bred by E. L. Lewis and Son. *Greatheart* weighed 658 kg at 500 days against a breed average of 550 kg and was reserve Bull of the Year in 1973-74.

Preface

This book is one of a series on livestock production which aims to explain simply and attractively the principles and practice of beef production. It is designed primarily for students, past and present, of the county colleges of agriculture, who are studying or actually engaged in beef farming.

It is hoped that former students will find much to refresh their memories and a useful guide to current techniques. Present students may use the book in conjunction with their lecture notes and as background reading.

Unlike pig production, the beef industry is more traditional and less liable to sudden change in techniques but, nevertheless, systems do alter and today barley beef and weight recordings – almost unheard of twenty years ago – are now accepted as general practice. Also, the type of animal butchers look for today with an emphasis on lean meat content are vastly different from the thick-set rather fat animals produced a decade or so ago.

To this end students and farmers alike cannot accept anything for granted and must always be seeking for new ideas and improved techniques based on sound husbandry. Remember, however, that the 'stockman's eye' is still as important as ever. Good stockmanship begins with good observation and working with stock. Careful observation, asking questions and thinking about the answers are the best ways to learning more about your chosen subject.

If anybody wishes to contact the author on any matter, they are invited to address any correspondence to him care of the publishers.

Chapter One
Thé Beef Industry

Beef is the most important and popular of the red meats. It provides more energy and protein per kilogram than other meats and is in greater demand than pork, mutton, poultry or fish.

Meat consumption

Beef is available in many forms: it can be purchased as fresh meat, chilled, frozen, or canned. Beef is an expensive food to produce and consequently to buy. Its consumption is highest in countries with a high national income.

Meat consumption per capita in UK 1974

	kg carcass weight
Beef and veal	22·3
Mutton and lamb	7·7
Pork	11·9
Bacon	9·3
Poultry meat	11·7

Adapted from Ministry of Agriculture.

Beef and veal consumption per capita in other European countries 1970

	kg carcass weight
France	30
Belgium/Luxembourg	27
West Germany	24·4
Italy	24·2
Netherlands	19·7
Denmark	19·7
Republic of Ireland	19·0

Fresh beef

The housewife prefers to buy fresh meat from the family butcher or self-service refrigerated display counters in the supermarket.

Fresh beef means that, following slaughter, the carcass is 'hung' for about seven to ten days and then sold to the general public. 'Hanging' beef in a refrigerated room at 4°C improves the eating quality of the beef.

Fresh meat is easily recognized by its appearance. It will have a bright colour and moist texture.

Chilled beef

Chilling consists of rapid reduction in temperature of the carcass from blood heat to just about freezing. During storage chilled beef undergoes a maturing process similar to hanging fresh, home-produced meat, though the lower temperature may slow down this process.

Most of our imported supplies of chilled beef come from South America, New Zealand and Australia. This means that the meat is 'maturing' for around four to six weeks during the voyage and getting to the shops.

During chilling, very little damage is done to the muscle fibres and when thoroughly dried out its appearance is similar to fresh beef.

Frozen beef

Beef may either be frozen in 'quarters of beef', i.e. the carcass divided into four parts, or it can be cut up into small joints, wrapped in polythene bags and then frozen.

With quarters of beef freezing is a slow process because the outer layers of fat act as an insulator and slow down the passage of cold air.

Furthermore, freezing large pieces of meat can cause some shrinking and distorting of muscle fibres due to water passing through the thin membranes around the muscle tissue. On defrosting not all of this water is reabsorbed and so there is a 'drip' of water and blood.

This discoloration associated with frozen beef after thawing makes this category of beef less popular with the general public.

On the other hand beef which is jointed and then frozen in domestic deep freezes is extremely popular with the general public. On thawing in the home the meat is very similar to fresh meat purchased from the butcher.

This is due to the rapid freezing and thawing of the small joint as compared with the quarter of beef.

Canned beef and manufactured products

A proportion of beef animals produce carcasses which are unsuitable for the fresh meat trade. These are usually from the older animals, cull cows and bulls no longer required for breeding. The meat is processed and in some cases artificial colouring is added. The meat is then tinned or canned – hence corned or bully beef.

Some carcasses are also used for sausage, beefburgers, mince, meat pies, meat paste, etc.

Meat retailers

The housewife has the choice of purchasing her meat either from a family butcher, or a self-service refrigerated display counter in a grocery store or supermarket.

The family butcher offers a personal service to the shopper, and is always willing to advise his customers on the most suitable joints for their needs. Indeed, the success of the butcher depends largely upon his ability to select and purchase livestock that will yield the type of meat cuts demanded by his customers.

The supermarkets display pre-packed, boneless joints, with a brief description, weight and price.

The housewife, generally speaking, is unable to recognize the cuts, and therefore selects her joint solely on appearance and price.

However, for the busy housewife with perhaps a full- or part-time job, the supermarket offers a great saving in time. The pre-packing, self-service food counters are rapidly gaining favour today.

The housewife

The general trend amongst housewives is to buy a small tender joint of meat for the Sunday roast and to rely on chops, steak, sausage and offals which can all be prepared quickly for the mid-week meals. This means that the housewife tends to buy the more 'expensive' parts of the carcass – grilling meat such as steak, chops and gammon are in greater demand than brisket of beef, scrag of mutton, or belly pork. This demand often leads to problems for the retailer in that selling the cheap joints, especially those used for stewing and boiling, is difficult.

There is almost universal demand for lean meat, and quite often the housewife will insist upon lean cuts to the detriment of flavour. Some fat is desirable in meat to aid cooking, but the customer does not always understand this, and will complain when the lean meat she buys from a self-service counter proves to be tough.

The housewife also takes particular note of the colour of meat. A light, pinky colour indicates freshness, and shows that the joint is cut from a young animal. As an animal gets older the colour of the muscle darkens (see page 37). Older meat may be tougher, but will have a better flavour than very young meat. However, there is some evidence to suggest that the public is not particularly interested in flavour.

Hanging meat in a coldroom at 4°C for two weeks after slaughter will improve flavour and make the meat more tender. This is due to enzyme action in the carcass. Unfortunately, when meat is hung, the colour is affected and the end product has a rather dark appearance which is less attractive to the customer.

Butchers and meat buyers for supermarkets are very much aware of the housewife's demands for lean and tender meat, and so many buyers purchase only lightweight, quickly grown animals. Thus the more saleable beef animals are the baby beeves (400–450 kg) which yield a higher proportion of the 'expensive' joints (for example sirloin, rump and rounds) with a minimum amount of fat, than would the more traditional animal of 550–600 kg.

Catering trade

Since the end of the Second World War, there has been an enormous change in the eating habits of the British public. Many school children are provided with a cooked midday meal at school. Office and factory workers have canteens and many businessmen enjoy expense-account lunches. Restaurants, snack bars, and even 'hot dog' stands have 'mushroomed' all over the country. There is no doubt that in an affluent society, families enjoy eating out regularly, and if the current trend continues, we may even see the whole family enjoying their Sunday roast in a competitively priced restaurant.

The catering trade can handle the larger joint of meat that is produced from medium to heavy weight stock. Chefs can carve an 8-kg sirloin that would hardly go into a housewife's oven.

The effect of the present demand from caterers for the heavier animal is to balance to some extent the production of fat stock. In consequence, some producers find it more profitable to raise medium weight animals, even if this means accepting a slightly lower price per kilogram.

Home supplies

Table 4 shows the total supplies of meat in the United Kingdom. Home production has increased substantially since 1946–7.

Pre-war we produced about 50 per cent of our meat requirements. By 1959 two-thirds of our needs were produced at home, as they still are today. Yet, despite this tremendous increase in production, the United Kingdom still remains the largest single importing country for meat in the world.

Table 1   Imports of beef and veal into the United Kingdom (thousand tons)

	1970	1971	1972	1973	1974
Beef					
Boneless					
Australia	31·0	30·1	65·6	83·0	22·6
Argentina	57·6	38·1	62·7	58·5	27·7
Other countries	53·3	60·0	63·4	67·0	82·2
Total (a)	141·8	128·2	191·6	208·5	132·5
Bone-in					
Fresh					
Irish Republic	87·3	87·4	63·5	26·5	26·7
Other countries	9·4	12·5	0·8	4·5	22·1
Total (a)	9.67	99·9	64·3	31·0	48.8

Chilled					
Denmark	*		*	1·9	20·3
Irish Republic	9·2	9·1	7·9	15·3	25·8
Yugoslavia	1·2	0·9			
Other countries	3·9	4·9	1·4	1·7	9·4(b)
Total (a)	14·3	15·0	9·3	19·0	55·4
Frozen					
Irish Republic	0·7	0·2	0·5	0·2	4·0
Australia	0·2	0·3	1·4	0·5	*
New Zealand	2·5	2·0	2·1	2·5	0·3
Other countries	3·9	2·3	1·5	0·9	1·2
Total (a)	7·3	4·8	5·5	4·2	5·5
Veal	0·5	0·9	2·7	3·3	3·1
Total beef and veal	260·6	248·8	273·4	266·0	245·3

(a) Because of individual rounding, figures do not necessarily add up to total shown.
(b) Of which West Germany provided 8·2.
* Negligible.

Source: Meat and Livestock Commission.

Table 2 Imports of canned meat into the United Kingdom (thousand tons)

	1970	*1971*	*1972*	*1973*	*1974*
Beef					
Tongues	2·2	2·1	1·5	1·0	0·6
Corned beef	45·8	41·7	48·5	43·6	36·4
Other	9·9	11·5	11·8	13·8	7·7
Veal	2·0	2·5	1·0	0·3	0·2
Total beef and veal (a)	59·9	57·7	62·8	58·7	45·0
Mutton and Lamb	2·6	5·4	2·7	1·4	0·9
Pig products					
Bacon and ham	29·2	31·8	30·3	37·7	36·1
Pork – ground or chopped	11·5	13·4	17·0	15·1	6·2

Pork – other	8·9	9·4	9·9	9·4	10·4
Tongues	1·1	1·6	1·5	1·2	1·2
Other	43·9	47·2	45·2	43·6	45·5
Total pig products (a)	94·5	103·3	104·0	107·0	99·4
Poultry	3·7	3·5	4·5	5·1	3·4
Other canned meat	2·5	2·3	2·7	0·8	0·7
Total canned meat (a)	163·2	172·2	176·6	173·0	149·5

(a) Because of individual rounding, figures do not necessarily add up to totals shown.

Source: Meat and Livestock Commission.

Table 3 UK Crop area (thousand hectares)

	June 1973	*June 1974*	*June 1975*
Wheat	1,146	1,233	1,204
Barley	2,268	2,214	2,286
Oats	281	253	253
Other cereals	57	48	45
Total cereals	3,752	3,748	3,788
Potatoes	225	215	215
Sugar beet	194	195	202
Oilseed rape	14	25	40
Beans for stock-feed	60	66	61
All other fodder	219	231	235
Orchard fruit	57	55	53
Vegetables, flowers, etc.	205	212	202
Small fruit	18	17	18
Other crops	13	14	14
Bare fallow	61	61	59
Total tillage	1,066	1,091	1,099
Temporary grass	2,346	2,316	2,276
Total arable	7,164	7,155	7,163
Permanent grass	4,914	4,920	4,897
Total crops and grass	12,078	12,075	12,060

Rough grazing	6,605	6,564	6,536
Total	18,683	18,639	18,596

Source: National Farmers Union.

Table 4   UK livestock numbers (thousand head)

	June 1973	June 1974	June 1975
Breeding cows–dairy	3,436	3,395	3,275
Breeding cows–beef	1,678	1,889	1,925
Total	5,114	5,285	5,200
Heifers in calf–dairy	671	723	650
Heifers in calf–beef	316	321	300
All other cattle	8,344	8,884	8,750
Total cattle	14,445	15,213	14,900
Sheep breeding flock (1)	13,654	13,865	13,900
All other sheep	14,289	14,633	14,700
Total sheep and lambs	27,943	28,498	28,600
Pig breeding herd	1,015	897	750
All other pigs	7,964	7,656	6,200
Total pigs	8,979	8,553	6,950
Poultry			
Growing pullets	18,808	18,958	18,400
Laying flock	51,766	50,100	49,400
Breeding flock	6,989	6,455	6,200
Broilers etc.	58,366	56,781	53,300
Ducks and geese	1,637	1,441	1,300
Turkeys	6,513	6,192	5,400
Total poultry	144,079	139,927	134,000

Source: National Farmers Union.

Chapter Two
Reproduction in Cattle

Female reproductive organs

The general construction of the cow's reproductive organs is shown in Fig. 1. These consist of the two *ovaries* which produce eggs or ova; the *fallopian tubes*, or oviducts, which convey the eggs after being released; the *uterus*, or womb, in which the eggs are implanted, and where the embryo will grow and develop; the *cervix* which forms a strong muscular collar that opens and closes the mouth of the uterus; the *vagina* which is a fairly large tube which connects the uterus to the *vulva* which is the external opening to the reproductive organs.

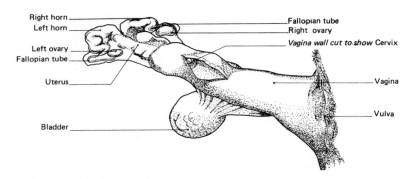

Fig. 1 Cow's reproductive system

Ovaries

The cow has two ovaries which are suspended by ligaments in the loin region of the body and are small oval shaped bodies, measuring about 25–35 mm across. The ovaries produce eggs or ova and various hormones which assist in reproduction and also affect changes in body growth.

The ova (eggs) are produced in sac-like structures called the Groffian follicles. The follicles also produce a fluid, so when the ovum is fully developed and the follicle ruptures, the fluid carries the ovum from the ovary to the fallopian tube in readiness for fertilization by the male sperm. This process is known as ovulation and occurs at regular intervals (usually every 21 days) when the cow is 'on heat'. The place of the ruptured follicle is taken by a substance known as the 'yellow body' or 'corpus luteum' which produces a hormone known as progesterone.

If the cow is mated and the ovum fertilized, the corpus luteum will persist and produce progesterone which will prevent the cow coming on heat and also stop the production of the follicles during the pregnancy. If the cow is not mated, or she fails to conceive, then the corpus luteum will disappear and normal production of follicles will continue.

Fallopian tubes

Linking the ovaries and the uterus together are the fallopian tubes (often referred to as the oviducts because they are used to convey the ova to the uterus) which terminate at the horns of the uterus. Fertilization of the sperm and the ova usually takes place in the fallopian tube.

Uterus

The uterus or womb is the largest part of the reproductive tract. Its function is to provide a home for the fertilized egg(s) until it develops into a fully grown calf. In cattle this 'growing period', or 'gestation', is approximately 280 days (about nine months) although this often varies by as much as 7–10 days either way.

Immediately after the ova is fertilized by the male sperm the egg begins to grow and at the same time passes down the fallopian tube into the uterus. The egg attaches itself to the wall of the uterus; a thin 'skin' or 'placenta' is then formed around the growing egg which is now called the embryo. The placenta then produces 'buttons' or cotyledons, which attach themselves to the wall of the uterus and through which food is passed to the growing calf via the navel cord or umbilicus.

It can be seen, therefore, that the calf is not connected directly to the cow, but is carried and fed inside the placenta.

At birth or parturition the placenta is broken and the calf delivered without this covering. Later the placenta, now called the 'after-birth' or cleansing is discharged from the uterus and the cow is said to have cleansed.

Cervix

This is a strong muscular collar that opens and closes the mouth of the uterus. It is normally closed to prevent infection entering the uterus, but is open during oestrus or 'heat period' to allow the sperms to enter, and also at parturition to allow the calf to be born. The opening and closing mechanism is controlled by various hormones which stimulate the cervix to dilate and contract.

Vagina

The vagina is a fairly large tube which connects the uterus to the external opening called the *vulva*. There is a small opening in it which is connected to the bladder and is used to convey waste urine from the body. In the act of mating the vagina is where the bull's penis enters the reproductive tract to deposit semen in the uterus.

Vulva

The vulva is the external opening of the tract and comprises two lateral lips or labia.

Male reproductive organs

The essential parts of the male reproductive organs are the two testicles or *testes* which produce the sperms; the two *vas deferens* or *spermatic cords* down which the sperms travel; three sets of glands which produce fluid substances to form the semen in which the sperms swim; the urethra, which is a passage through which both urine and sperms pass; and the penis, which when protruded is used for implanting the sperms in the female during mating or *service*.

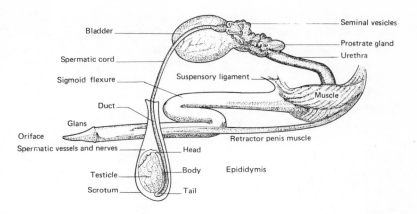

Fig. 2 Bull's reproductive system

Testicles

The bull, like other male farm animals, has two testicles which are suspended outside the body, but enclosed in a sac or scrotum. The normal temperature of the testicles is about 0·1°C less than the body; the scrotum is outside the body in order to regulate the temperature. In cold weather the scrotum contracts thus bringing the testicles nearer to the body and in hot conditions the scrotum expands. It is possible in some males that the testicles are found in the abdominal cavity and do not descend into the scrotum. When this happens, or if only one testicle descends, the calf is known as a rig.

The function of the testicles is to produce live sperms which are single free moving cells that are capable of uniting with the female ovum to produce a fertilized egg. Also the testicles produce the male sex hormone *testosterone* which is responsible for inducing the desire to mate and the secondary sex characteristics. Thus the entire male will be masculine in appearance, whereas if the bull calf is castrated (surgical removal of the testicles, see page 80) the castrate or steer will have a feminine appearance and show no interest in mating.

Sperms

Large numbers of sperms are produced in the testicles in the *seminiferous tubules*. The sperms pass from the tubules into a coiled tube attached to the rear of the testicle and called the *epididymis*. The sperms are stored for a short period in the epididymis where they mature and then they pass into the vas deferens which is a duct leading back into the body cavity and connecting to the urethra.

As the sperms move along the vas deferens, or spermatic cords, they mix with fluids produced in the 'accessory' glands, namely the prostate gland, the seminal vesicle, and Cowper's gland. These fluids mix with the sperms and act as a carrier. The fluid is now called semen. The bull produces approximately 5 cc of semen at each ejaculation.

Urethra and penis

The two vas deferens or spermatic cords join together to form the urethra, which is a long tube that connects the bladder to the penis, and, therefore, acts as a common vessel for both urine and semen. The penis is the final part of the reproductive tract and is normally retained in a loose fold of skin – the prepuce or sheath. It is formed of *erectile tissue* which contains spaces which can be filled with blood. In the act of mating the penis becomes filled with blood so that it is rigid and can penetrate the female vagina.

Artificial insemination

Artificial insemination, usually referred to as A.I., is widely used in dairy herds and to some extent in pure-bred beef herds too. Usually, however, the farmer with a large herd of beef cows finds it more convenient to keep a bull.

The A.I. service is operated in this country mainly by the Milk Marketing Board but there are also some independent centres. Table 5 shows the number of beef and dairy inseminations for England and Wales 1974–5.

At the A.I. centre only top quality bulls in full health are used. The semen is collected from the bull by means of an artificial vagina which consists of a cylinder into which a rubber tube rather like the inner tube of a motor tyre is inserted. The ends of the tube are folded over so that the space between the cylinder and tube may be filled with air and water at blood temperature.

By the skilful use of a dummy cow the bull is induced to 'serve' and the operator diverts the bull's penis into the artificial vagina to collect his semen.

Once the semen is collected it is taken into the laboratory for careful examination and dilution.

Semen contains millions of sperms and so can be diluted and divided into large numbers. An average bull producing 5 cc of semen will provide sufficient sperm for 200–400 cows and an above-average bull can provide sufficient sperm for 600 cows in a single service!

Table 5   Breed demand (Board centres) April 1974–March 1975

Breed	First Inseminations					
	Number			*% of Total*		
	1973/4	*1974/5*	*Difference*	*1973/4*	*1974/5*	*1964/5*
Ayrshire	2,3173	22,216	− 957	1·2	1·2	5·1
Friesian	1,159,431	1,010,966	−148,465	58·5	55·0	49·0
Guernsey	31,116	30,903	− 213	1·6	1·7	4·3
Jersey	28,262	27,388	− 874	1·4	1·5	3·4
R & W Friesian	1,979	1,920	− 59	0·1	0·1	
Dairy	1,243,961	1,093,393	−150,568	62·8	59·5	62·4
Brown Swiss		50	+ 50		0·0	
British White		1	+ 1		0·0	
Dexter	43	58	+ 15	0·0	0·0	
Kerry						
Meuse-Rhine-Issel	345	383	+ 38	0·0	0·0	
Red Dane	731	528	− 203	0·0	0·0	0·0
Red Poll	502	432	− 70	0·0	0·0	0·0
Shorthorn	6,620	5,596	− 1,024	0·4	0·3	1·5
N. Dairy Shorthorn	48	46	− 2	0·0	0·0	0·1
Welsh Black	9,525	9,030	− 495	0·5	0·6	0·7
Gloucester	24	23	− 1	0·0	0·0	
Dual Purpose	27,594	24,922	− 2,672	1·4	1·4	2·6
Aberdeen Angus	93,621	88,535	− 5,086	4·7	4·8	8·3
Beevbilde	4		− 4	0·0	0·0	
Blonde d'Aquitaine	3,935	4,385	+ 450	0·2	0·2	
Brahman		2	+ 2		0·0	
Beef Shorthorn	497	354	− 143	0·0	0·0	0·0
Charolais	136,569	114,617	− 21,952	6·9	6·3	1·7
Chianina	5,944	7,787	+ 1,843	0·3	0·4	
Chartley						
Devon	15,778	14,549	− 1,229	0·8	0·8	2·1
Gelbvieh	328	438	+ 110	0·0	0·0	
Hereford	370,150	419,962	+ 49,812	18·7	22·9	22·1
Highland	105	14	− 14	0·0	0·0	
Longhorn	18	16	− 2	0·0	0·0	
Limousin	13,199	12,514	− 685	0·7	0·7	
Lincoln Red	1,486	1,135	− 351	0·1	0·1	0·1

Luing	427	389	−	38	0·0	0·0	
Marchigiana		33	+	33		0·0	
Maine Anjou	661	535	−	126	0·0	0·0	
Murray Grey	1,292	3,756	+	2,464	0·1	0·2	
Romagnola		304	+	304		0·0	
Simmental	56,807	41,682	−	15,125	2·9	2·3	
Sussex	6,477	6,214	−	263	0·3	0·3	0·5
Galloway	1,566	1,460	−	106	0·1	0·1	0·2
Beef	708,864	718,758	+	9,894	35·8	39·1	35·0
Total	1,980,419	1,837,073		−143,346	100·0	100·0	100·0

Source: Milk Marketing Board.

Once the semen is diluted it is placed in 'straws' or 'pellets', deep frozen and stored in liquid nitrogen at −192°C. Deep frozen sperms can live for many years and so it is possible to keep a bull's semen until his first calves have been reared and proven of merit or, in the case of particularly valuable animals, the semen may be used for years after the bull's death.

Preparation of cow

The technique of A.I. is fairly straightforward, but if maximum conception rates are to be obtained certain rules must be followed. Firstly it is most important to detect when the cow is properly on heat, see page 98. When you are quite sure she is properly in season, bring her indoors and either tie her up or put her in a small cubicle stall with a sound back gate.

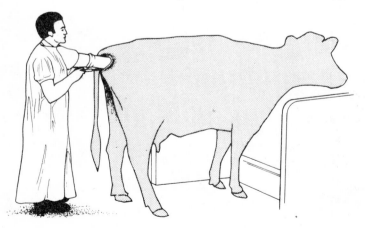

Fig. 3 Cow in stall ready for A.I.

Telephone the A.I. centre as early as possible and if you are unable to be present leave clear directions as to which building the cow is in, and tie a label with the cow's name on her tail or over her stall.

Also you should provide a clean towel, soap and bucket of warm water for the inseminator to wash his hands and boots.

On arrival the inseminator will take a 'straw' of semen from a flask of liquid nitrogen and when it is thawed will place the straw into the cervix and inseminate the cow.

Chapter Three
Growth and Development

An understanding of the principles of the growth and development of farm animals is of immense value to the farmer and stockman. For it is the way in which an animal grows and its subsequent development that eventually determine the final appearance and quality of the carcass. Animals that grow quickly are usually better at converting food into meat than slow growers. Stock that are managed badly through their early life rarely make satisfactory progress in the later fattening stages and produce carcasses inferior in quality to stock that are fed well. In this chapter we shall see how the farmer is able to influence the final appearance and carcass quality by his selection and management of the stock in his care.

The late Dr John Hammond defined growth in farm animals as 'the increase in weight of an animal, until a mature size is reached'.

Development is defined as the change in body shape or conformation. Development also includes changes in body structure, for example, development of mammary tissue in the pregnant female.

Growth and development before birth

Life begins at conception, with the union of the male sperm and the female egg. Each parent contributes substantially one half to the inheritance of the offspring.

In the early stages of pregnancy, the developing foetus is surrounded by large amounts of fluids and tissue.

In the later stages of pregnancy, the unborn animal makes rapid growth in size and weight, its bulk replacing much of the fluids.

It is important, therefore, that all pregnant stock should receive adequate nutrition during the final stages of gestation, in order that the developing animal is sufficiently well grown and is strong and active at birth. Supplementary feeding of cows before calving is known amongst farmers as 'steaming up'.

As a general guide we may say that two-thirds of the growth (increase in live-weight) takes place in the last one-third of the pregnancy.

The size of the offspring at birth is controlled by factors other than nutrition during pregnancy. The more important of these are sex, breed and single or multiple births. Thus, Aberdeen Angus calves are smaller than South Devons. Twin calves are lighter than singles, although their total weight may amount to more.

Size at birth is also controlled by the dam, due to a special substance in the mother's blood-stream. This substance prevents the foetus from growing to such a size as to prevent parturition. Were it not for this control, the mating of a large breed like the Charolais to a small breed like the Jersey would give rise to difficulties at birth. These do not occur except in exceptional circumstances.

Growth after birth

After birth, growth is usually measured as kilograms daily live-weight gain (d.l.w.g.) or weekly live-weight gain (w.l.w.g.).

In all animals, the growth rate is slow to begin with, and then rises quite rapidly but slows again as maturity is reached.

If the d.l.w.g. is plotted against the age of the animal on a graph, then we get a characteristic S curve.

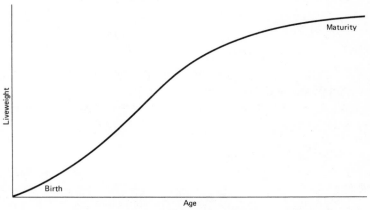

Fig. 4 (a) Curve of live-weight growth of farm animals (McMeekan 1943)

The S curve is similar in all farm livestock, but the degree of steepness in the curve will vary according to the breed and strain of animal.

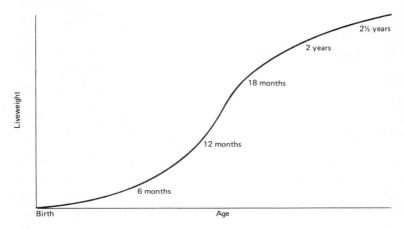

Fig. 4 (b)   Curve of live-weight growth of cattle

From the graphs we can see that cattle grow fastest at somewhere between three months of age and fifteen to eighteen months. This will vary considerably between breeds, and even between individual animals.

If cattle are fed wisely during this growth period, maximum live-weight gain and, it is hoped, maximum profitability should occur.

Changes in body proportions (waves of growth)

At birth, the head is relatively large, the legs are long, and the body small (see Fig. 5(a)). In the mature or fully grown animal, the head is small and the legs short in proportion to the body (see Fig. 5(b)).

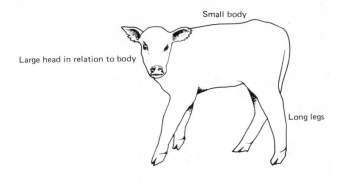

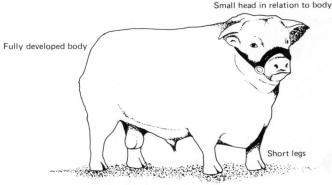

Fig. 5 (b)   Changes in body proportions: adult

These changes in body shape are due to different parts growing at different rates. The head and legs are early to develop (skeleton), while the body, particularly the hindquarters and loin region, are late developing and are the last parts to reach mature size.

The body, which is later to become the carcass, consists of three main tissues, *bone* which forms the skeleton, *muscle* which is the lean, red meat, and *fat*.

These three tissues grow in a very definite order. Bone is the first to develop, muscle is intermediate but tends to follow bone fairly closely, while fat is the last to develop and grows fastest as the animal approaches maturity.

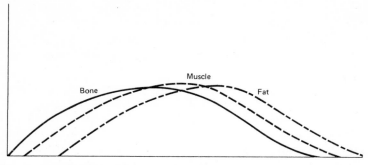

Fig. 6 Waves of growth of the main tissues

The young animal, therefore, contains a higher proportion of bone and muscle and a lower percentage of fat than the older animal.

This knowledge is of vital importance to meat producers, since the present day demand is for young, tender, lean meat. It can readily be appreciated that if livestock are fed on a high plane of nutrition during their early life, then the final carcass will have the maximum proportion of muscle. If the animal is slaughtered before it reaches maturity it will contain relatively little fat.

Early maturity

Early maturing breeds are those in which the waves of growth are steep, and follow each other closely. Such breeds fatten at light weights and at early ages. The Aberdeen Angus breed is a good example of early maturity.

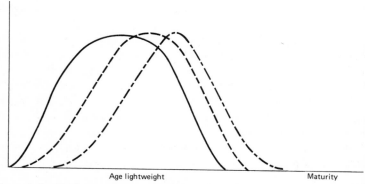

Fig. 7 (a) Early maturity, e.g. Aberdeen Angus

Late maturity

Late maturing animals, like the Friesian steer, may grow fast in terms of d.l.w.g., but, because their waves of growth are wider apart than early maturing stock, they take longer to fatten and mature. This accounts for the popularity of pure-bred Friesian steers, kept on the barley beef system. The steers are fed on a high plane of nutrition that induces the development of bone and muscle at a very fast rate. The steers are slaughtered well before maturity (10–12 months) to avoid the laying down of fat.

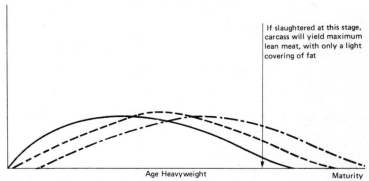

Fig. 7 (b)   Late maturity, e.g. British Friesian

Changes in internal organs

In addition to the changes that take place in the body, similar waves of growth exist in the internal organs. The main body organs develop in the following pattern – first the brain, secondly the heart, and thirdly the digestive system. The reproductive organs and mammary tissue do not develop until much later.

. In cattle the calf has a well developed brain at birth, its lungs are well developed and so is the heart. The digestive system, however, does not fully develop until the calf is three weeks old. The reproductive organs start to function at puberty, which is about 8–9 months in bulls, perhaps a little earlier in heifers. The mammary tissue, that is the udder, develops very little until the heifer is in calf and continues to develop during the subsequent lactations.

Offals and dressing percentage

When the animal is slaughtered, most of the internal organs are utilized as offal.

Young animals will have a higher proportion of offals in relation to carcass weight than will the older animal. This explains why young stock have a lower dressing percentage than older stock.

Growth changes in the beef carcass

The present-day requirements range from small, well-fleshed carcasses of around 250–300 kg (lightweight) up to the heavier 400–500 kg carcasses which have been quickly grown. The butcher always selects carcasses with the highest proportion of 'expensive' joints. These are the loin, ribs, rump and rounds. The 'cheap' joints are the clod, neck, brisket and flank.

When selecting live cattle, the butcher looks for blocky, thickset animals with short, thick bone. This will give a carcass with blocky joints and great depth of muscle. (See Chapter 4.)

Fine bone is associated with poor fleshing in all classes of farm stock, e.g. Jersey cattle.

Evaluation of the carcass

Muscle tissue

Muscles are made up of fibres, arranged in bundles. As the fibre grows, the muscle bundle enlarges. This causes the meat texture to become coarse and less tender.

Some parts of the carcass, such as the sirloin and rump steak,

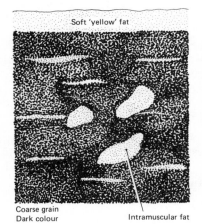

Soft 'yellow' fat

creamy white – firm fat

Coarse grain
Dark colour

Intramuscular fat

Fine grain
Light 'pinky' colour with moist appearance

Fig. 8 (a)   Coarse grained meat – lower quality
Fig. 8 (b)   Fine grained meat – best quality

are more tender and have a finer grain than the other parts in the same carcass, such as the shin, which is very coarse and tough.

Colour of muscle

The colour of muscle in the young animal is always lighter than that of older stock. This is due to a pigment that is released in the movement of the animal. Thus the more exercise that the animal receives during its lifetime, the darker will be the colour of the muscle. Exercise also strengthens muscle fibres which causes the grain to become coarse and the meat tough.

Veal calves produce light coloured carcasses. Pork is always lighter than beef or mutton.

Flavour is also associated with the same pigment that affects colour in meat. Thus in the older animal the flavour is more pronounced, but the meat will be tougher to eat. Likewise, very young meat such as veal, spring lamb, broiler chicken or pork tend to lack flavour although, of course, they will be extremely tender.

Fat

During the beef calf's early life fat is deposited first on the gut and kidney regions; next the fat develops in a layer over the muscle. This gives a smooth, firm appearance to the well finished beast. Lastly, the fat penetrates the muscle bundles and causes 'marbling', a term that butchers use to describe the intramuscular fat.

Marbling is desirable in the older animal, since in breaking up the muscle fibres, the fat tenderizes the meat. Marbling is said to aid cooking as the fat melts and so bastes the muscle during the cooking period.

In young stock, marbling is not thought to be necessary, and certainly there is a marked reluctance by the public to buy meat that carries too much fat.

Colour of fat

The colour of fat is a reflection of growth changes. The yellow colour sometimes seen in carcasses is caused by feeding foods containing carotene.

Grass fed cattle have a marked yellow fat, whilst cattle fattened in yards have a white, firm fat. If stock are allowed to lose condition then they utilize fat from their bodies. The yellow colour, however, remains. If cattle go through periods of 'rise and fall' in condition before slaughter, then the final carcass will be extremely yellow.

Quality and flavour of fat are largely gauged by firmness and colour. The public like white, firm fat and so do the butchers who 'hang' beef for one or two weeks in a refrigerator. Soft yellow fat, apart from having a displeasing appearance, is likely to go rancid and absorb taints.

Feedingstuffs affect fats in various ways. Maize fed in large amounts will cause a soft yellow fat. Foods like barley, skim milk, fish meal, peas and beans produce firm white fats.

Use of synthetic oestrogens and their effect on growth

The use of synthetic oestrogens to caponize poultry has been practised in this country since 1943. It has long been known that the administration of female sex hormones into the blood stream of poultry increases the amount of fat circulating in the blood stream. Also in cockerels the hormones suppress the growth of comb and wattle and make them sterile and more docile. Thus chemical castration is achieved by simply implanting a 12 mg pellet. It is claimed that capons are more tender and of better quality than cockerels.

In 1949 F. N. Andrews published results of lambs treated with implants of stilboestrol which showed quite clearly that implanted lambs grew more quickly than the controls.

Mode of action

Unlike the experience with poultry, the use of oestrogens with cattle and sheep does not increase internal fat deposits, but rather reduces the amount of fat and increases the lean content. There is an increase in carcass protein, bone and water. The action of the hormone is to stimulate the *pituitary* gland to release growth-provoking substances. Hence growth is stimulated and fattening discouraged.

See Fig. 4(a) (page 31) for normal growth curve in fattening animal.

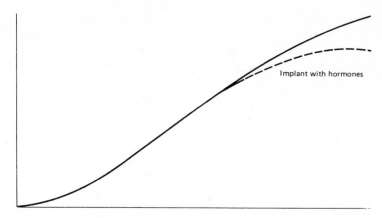

Implant with hormones

Fig. 9   Action of hormones on growth

Fig. 9 shows how hormones have the effect of delaying maturity. This encourages the production of bone and muscle, but delays the production of excess fat.

Choice of hormone

There is little to choose between hexoestrol or stilboestrol as far as stock is concerned, but because of the effect on men handling the tablets, hexoestrol is recommended.

Dose rate

60 mg is recommended for steers fattened indoors, while 35–40 mg is sufficient if the animals are at pasture.

Implantation should be carried out about 100 days before slaughter if the maximum benefit is to be obtained.

Site of implantation

The best site is the loose base of the ear. This is easily reached when the animal is held in a cattle crush, or something similar. Under the tail is an alternative site, but is not recommended. Any pellet residues left in the ear after slaughter are disposed of in waste by-products such as fertilizer.

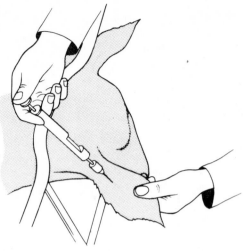

Fig. 10   Implanting tablets in base of ear

Mode of implantation

Oestrogens may be administered either as pellets, or in a semi-paste form, the latter method requiring a hypodermic syringe.

Oral administration

This is popular in the United States of America where yard fattening is widely practised. It is obviously easier to add the oestrogen to the feed, although the method is less effective than implantation. It is usual to feed 10 mg per day for 100 days before slaughter.

Advantages of oestrogens

Feeding trials have shown, generally, an increase in live-weight over control groups of 15–30 per cent. Also there may be an increase in food efficiency which represents a further saving in food cost.

Disadvantages

Side effects of implantation in bullocks were a distinct disadvantage in the earlier days when large doses were used, since it often caused bellowing, teat development and a raising of the tail head. This will only occur if the recommended dose is exceeded.

The flesh is made noticeably paler in colour and it contains more water. It is claimed to be more tender, but perhaps lacks flavour.

Pasture residue

Some concern has been expressed at the possibility of oestrogen excreted by animals accumulating in the soil and pastures over a period of time. Experiments have shown that soil bacteria break down the oestrogens and these, so it is claimed, are lost in the ground.

Chapter Four
The Butcher's Beast

Selection of cattle for slaughter

When selecting cattle for slaughter, the butcher takes into consideration the breed, age, weight, health, dressing percentage, general conformation, quality and finish.

Dressing percentage

This indicates the carcass yield, or the amount of carcass the butcher will have for sale. Well finished cattle will have a high killing out percentage (k.o. %) while under-fattened beasts will be low.

Type of stock	Dressing %	Remarks
Store cattle	50–51	Unsuitable for slaughter
Lean, half finished cattle	52–54	Suitable for certain trades
Prime cattle	56–58	Ideal for present day requirements
'Smithfield show' cattle	60+	Over finished, too much waste fat for present day demand

Age

Age is roughly determined by examining the incisor teeth, which are termed broad teeth. In small calves we look for either the navel cord, or horn buds.

	Age	Evidence of Age
Baby calves	birth–7 days	Navel cord dries up and drops off
	7–21 days	Scar left where navel cord was attached to belly

	21–28 days	In horned breeds the horn buds can be felt emerging through the skull
Yearlings	$1\frac{1}{2}$–$1\frac{3}{4}$ years	Two broad teeth
Two year olds	2–$2\frac{1}{2}$ years	Four broad teeth
Adult	3–$3\frac{1}{4}$ years	Six broad teeth
Fully grown stock	$3\frac{1}{2}$–4 years	Eight broad teeth

The age at which broad teeth appear will vary according to the breed and the method of rearing. For example, single suckled Hereford calves will often show their first broad teeth at around sixteen months, whilst Friesian calves reared on the early weaning system may not show their first teeth until 19–20 months old.

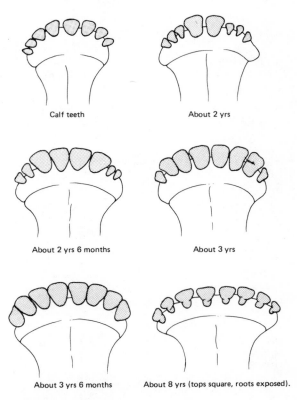

Calf teeth

About 2 yrs

About 2 yrs 6 months

About 3 yrs

About 3 yrs 6 months

About 8 yrs (tops square, roots exposed).

Fig. 11 Dentition of cattle

Conformation

Conformation is the general outline or contour of the body. Butchers prefer animals with compact, well fleshed blocky conformation.

Finish

Finish indicates the thickness of flesh in the live animals. In the carcass it refers to the depth of muscle, colour and covering of fat.

Quality

Quality is a combination of finish, texture, colour and firmness of fat, marbling (intramuscular fat) and proportion to meat to bone.

Prime sides of beef

The butcher looks for a compact, well fleshed young carcass, with a high proportion of red meat to fat and bone. A smooth covering of creamy white fat is desirable. A good carcass will cut approximately 60 per cent by weight, prime joints, i.e. rump, rounds, sirloin, etc. and 40 per cent coarse cuts, i.e. brisket, flank, clod, etc.

Points and joints

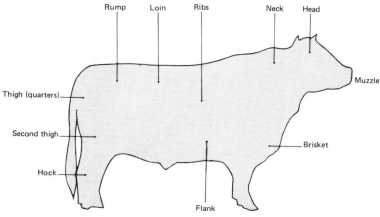

Fig. 12 (a) Points of a beef beast

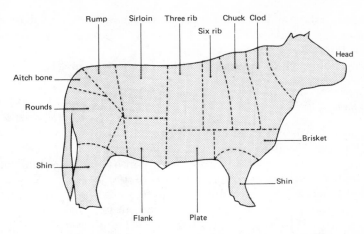

Fig. 12 (b) Beef joints (There is some variation, from one part of the country to another, in the method of cutting up the carcass and in the names given to the various parts. The ones used here are, however, those generally used.)

Categories of beef

Stock	Approx. age at slaughter	Showing not more than
Mature steers and heifers	2½–3½ years	six broad teeth
Prime steers and heifers	18–24 months	two broad teeth
Baby beef intensively produced	12–15 months	no broad teeth
Young bulls	12–14 months	no broad teeth
Cow heifers – S.Y.C.	3 years	six broad teeth
Fat cows	4–10 years	full mouth
Fat bulls	3–10 years	full mouth
Calves – veal	4–28 days	
Calves – Dutch veal	12–16 weeks	

Mature beef

This is usually pure-bred beef cattle, 3–4 years old, 600–700 kg, which were once considered to be prime beef. The carcasses are

45

deeply fleshed and well marbled. The meat tends to be dark in colour and possesses a distinct flavour. Today these cattle are no longer popular, with the butcher because he can only cut large joints from such a carcass, and of course the present-day demand is for small, lean cuts.

Prime beef

Today our prime beef is produced from the beef × dairy breeds such as the Aberdeen Angus × Shorthorn. Steers are slaughtered at between 450–550 kg when 20–24 months old, and have an estimated dressing percentage of 56–58 per cent. Heifers are slaughtered at lighter weights, usually between 350–450 kg when 18–20 months old, with a similar dressing out percentage as steers.

This type of beast will yield a well finished, fine grained, medium coloured carcass, with a reasonable flavour.

Baby beef

Baby beef is supplied in two forms, firstly pure-bred single-suckled beef calves that are weaned and then fattened without a store period, and secondly from intensively fed barley beef. Both systems of production produce the type of meat that the housewife likes, namely tender, lean 'pinky' coloured meat. The butcher finds a ready sale for baby beef, and because the meat is so tender, he can sell much of the shoulder meat as roasting joints.

The single-suckled beef calves are sold at between 350–450 kg for steers and 300–400 kg for heifers when around 14–15 months old. Barley beef cattle reach 400–500 kg for steers and 350–450 kg for heifers at around 12–14 months old. Both types of cattle will dress out at approximately 56–57 per cent.

Young bulls – bull beef

On the Continent it has been the practice to raise entire bull calves for beef for many years. The advantages are that the entire bull grows faster, converts to food more efficiently and produces a leaner carcass than the castrate (steer). The disadvantages are that the growing bulls must be housed separately and are less docile than steers.

Young bulls will reach 500–550 kg in 12–13 months and dress out at 56–57 per cent.

Cow heifers – Special Young Cows (S.Y.C.)

These are females which have had one calf, but have not more than six broad teeth (about 3 years old). Although somewhat variable in quality, the better animals can produce very good beef. S.Y.C. vary in weight from 400–600 kg with k.o. percentage from 54–60 per cent.

Fat cows

Fat cows produce nearly half our home beef supplies, the majority being dairy cows. The quality is extremely variable and ranges from thin fleshed shelly animals like the Jersey which is only suitable for manufacturing, to the young deeply fleshed mature Friesian cow which in certain cases produces beef almost equal to that of mature steers.

Age, breed and k.o. percentage determine the value of fat cows. The poorest animals are worth very little, whilst the best cows will fetch almost as much as mature steers.

Fat bulls

Fat bulls are unsuitable for the fresh meat trade, and are used therefore for manufacturing purposes. The carcass is dark red in colour, coarse grained with a high proportion of fore end meat.

Calves

Calves are slaughtered as baby veal when a few days old, or as Dutch veal when around 12–16 weeks.

Baby veal is based on the supply of pure-bred bull calves from the dairy breeds which are unsuitable for rearing for beef. The calves may be killed when a few days old at approximately 35–45 kg l.w. or they can be fed whole milk until they reach 50–60 kg at about 3–4 weeks old.

Dutch veal

Dutch veal is a relatively new method of producing veal. Specially formulated milk replacement meals are fed to the calves in generous amounts to enable them to make maximum live-weight gain. Friesian bull calves will reach 100–150 kg carcass weight in less than four months. This type of veal is becoming increasingly popular.

Butcher's beast

Selecting cattle that are suitable for slaughter is an art that takes some time to acquire. The beginner should constantly handle fattening stock, noting the changes that occur in body size, shape and fleshing. As you feed and tend stock, it takes but a little time to run a hand over the ribs, across the loin, or down the hind quarters, but this experience of handling, the sense of touch in your finger tips and the constant visual observation will later prove invaluable when you come to assess the butcher's beast.

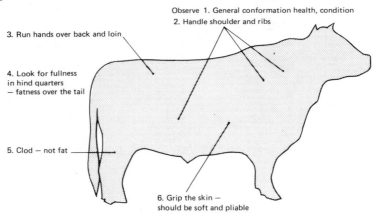

Fig. 13 Handling the butcher's beast

Before cattle are sent to market you must estimate the live-weight and dressing percentage. The live-weight will depend upon the type of stock you produce, i.e. baby beef, prime beef or mature cattle. The dressing percentage should be not less than 54 per cent and not more than 58 per cent. As a guide to dressing percentage, cattle that have a firm covering of flesh over the ribs are suitable for slaughter. A more thorough assessment would be:

1. Observe the general conformation of the animal. Butchers prefer stock that appear 'square' from in front and behind, and

48

rectangular when viewed from the side.

2. Handle the beast by running the flat of your hand over the ribs and shoulder. The flesh should be firm and evenly distributed in this area. If the beast is over-fat, then it will feel soft and fleshy.

3. Move to the loin, which should be wide and firm. Span your hands across the loin, noting the width, then prod the flesh with outstretched fingers to estimate the depth of muscle.

4. The loin should continue evenly into the rump, which is the most valuable part of the animal. Butchers look, therefore, for a long, wide rump. In over-fed animals the hock bones will be hardly visible but in commercial stock they should be clearly seen.

5. The hindquarters should be full of muscle which must be firm to touch. There should be no signs of soft, patchy fat in any part of the body. Over-fat heifers will be found patchy around the tail head.

6. Finally, handle the skin by grasping the hide on the sides or in the flank, or by pressing your fingers into the skin around the shoulders and over the ribs. The skin should feel soft and pliable; a poor hide will be harsh, tight and thick.

Carcass joints

Following slaughter, the beast is eviscerated and the hide removed. The carcass is then divided into fore quarters and hind quarters.

	%	
Carcass cold	58	Bone, muscle and fat
Edible offals	13	Heart, liver, lungs, stomach, etc.
Intestinal contents	14	Undigested and waste food, blood, etc.
Inedible offals	13	Skull, hooves, hide, horns, etc.
Shrinkage	2	Difference between hot carcass and cold carcass weight due to evaporation
Total	100	

The methods of cutting up a carcass into joints vary greatly from district to district and, indeed, between butchers within a town or village. The following account is typical of many Midland butchers' cutting technique.

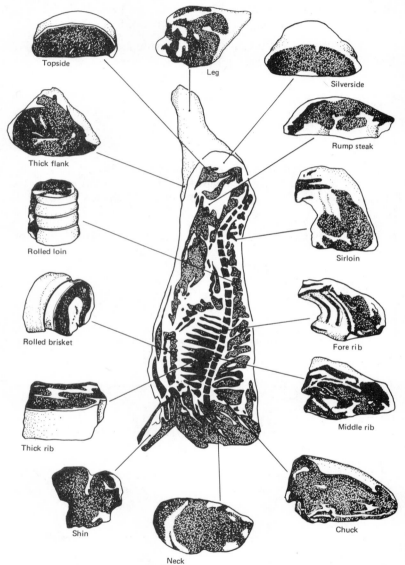

Fig. 14 (a) Side of beef, illustrating the various joints (Source: Meat and Livestock Commission)

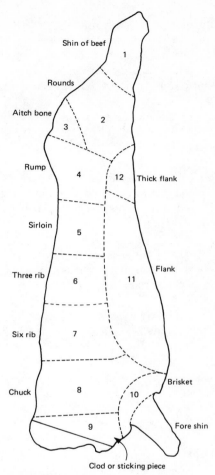

Fig. 14 (b)   Side of prime beef

Hind quarter

Aitchbone   (3) (5 kg) is a triangular piece cut from between the top of the rounds and the rump. Aitchbone is lean meat and makes a popular weekend roasting joint.

Rounds   (2). Topside and silverside (25 kg). These two cuts are divided by splitting the 'seam' between them. The topside forms the inner side of the leg, and consequently is more tender than the

51

silverside. Topside can be fried, but is generally sold as a roasting joint. Silverside, named because of its silvery colour caused by 'silver' muscle fibres running through the groin, is usually associated with pickling and boiling. Boiling will help to break down the connective tissue, thus making the meat more tender.

Rump (4) (10 kg) is the most valuable part of the carcass, due to its exceptional muscle texture. The rump is used almost exclusively for grilling steaks.

Sirloin (5) (25 kg) is a most attractive part of the carcass. It may be sold as T bone steaks, or as a roasting joint. Cuts of sirloin may be sold on the bone or boneless. The meat is usually well marbled in this area.

Three rib (7) (15 kg) consists of the last three ribs which are referred to as 'floating' ribs or wing ribs. This part may be roasted on the bone or sold boneless.

Thick flank (11) (10 kg) consists of mainly lean, but somewhat muscular, flesh. It may be rolled and then roasted, or used as stewing meat.

Hind shin or shank (1) (6 kg) is poor quality meat due to bundles of muscle fibre found in this part of the leg. It may be minced or sold for stewing.

Fore quarter

Clod and sticking piece (9) (15 kg). Except for very young beeves, these joints are of poor quality due to the development of neck muscles. The 'sticking piece' is usually minced while the clod is used for stewing.

Chuck (8) (30 kg) varies in quality according to the age of the beast. Young animals (12–14 months) produce first quality roasting or frying meat, but in the older animal ($2\frac{1}{2}$–3 years) the chuck makes second quality roasting beef.

Ribs (6) (25 kg) produce popular roasting joints, especially when cut from young beeves. In the older animal there is a tendency towards coarser meat. The joints are usually boned and rolled.

Thin flank (11) (7 kg) is similar to the thick flank – used for stewing and minced.

Brisket (10) (12 kg) varies enormously in quality between the various grades of fat stock. It may, at its best, be suitable for slow roasting, or if carefully boned out and the excess fat removed, used for salting and boiling. Poor quality brisket is boned, the fat removed and then minced.

Fore shin (13) (5 kg), very similar to hind shin, is used for stewing and mincemeat.

Edible offals

Ox-tail : used for making soup and stews.
Heart : generally roasted, but may be boiled or minced for sausage making.
Liver : frying, considered a delicacy.
Ox-cheek end head trimmings : stewing, mince, brown.
Sweetbreads (*thymus and pancreas*) *:* fried and boiled.
Spleen : used in pie making and for flavouring soups.
Blood : black puddings.
Fats : (a) Suet, used for making boiled puddings, suet pastry, mincemeat, etc. (b) Fat, rendered down for dripping.
Lungs : usually sold as cat food but may be used for faggots.
Udder : boiled or fried.
Kidneys : stewing, soup or fried.
Feet : boiled for 'cowsheel'.
Reticulem : tripe.
Tongue : boiled and served cold.

Inedible offals

These include the hide, which is cured for leather; the hair which makes brushes, felts or is used in upholstery; waste trimming, such as fat, blood, bone etc., which is manufactured into meat and bone manure, sterilized bone flour and ladies' cosmetics.

Chapter Five
Beef Production in the United Kingdom

There are three stages in the life of a beef animal – the calf-rearing stage, the growing stage and the finishing or fattening stage. The growing stage may include a store period, which means that in the winter the animal is fed on a moderate diet and subsequently grows rather slowly.

The traditional beef systems found in the United Kingdom follow a pattern closely related to the life of the beef animal. There are stockrearing farms where beef cows are kept solely for breeding and suckling their calves until these are six or eight months old. This system is referred to as single suckling. Stockrearing is usually found on poorer land such as the farms found in the upland and hill areas.

Farms where cattle are 'grown on', or kept for a store period, are found in marginal areas. A marginal farm is a holding situated geographically between the hill farm and the lowland farm.

Fattening farms fall into two categories: the grassland farm and the arable farm. To fatten cattle on grass, you must have rich, fertile pastures that will produce plenty of herbage throughout the summer months, especially during the drier periods of July and August.

The arable farmer fattens beef cattle during the winter months by keeping the stock in cattle yards and feeding them a diet of mainly home-grown cereals and cheap arable by-products such as pea haulm silage, sugar-beet tops and oat or barley straw. The cattle will lie on copious amounts of wheat straw, and so during the fattening period produce many tonnes of valuable farmyard manure which is needed on the arable land to restore and maintain soil fertility.

The choice of farming system depends very largely upon the altitude, climate, topography, vegetation, and by no means least, the soil.

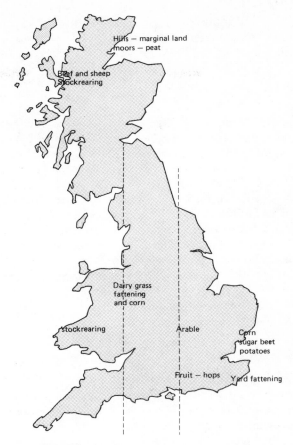

Fig. 15 Farming patterns in Britain

Climate

The average rainfall for the entire country is 1000 mm but this changes from 500–550 mm in the eastern counties to 600 mm in central England and to as high as 1500 mm in parts of Wales, N. Ireland and Scotland.

The westerly winds that blow in from the Atlantic and the mountainous ranges make the west coast a particularly high rainfall area. The distribution of sunshine shows a general decrease with altitude. Air temperature varies from as low as −9°C in winter to around 22–24°C in summer.

Thus we find southern England has the most hours of sunshine, is warmest in summer and relatively low in rainfall, while in Scotland, northern England and Wales it is generally very cold in winter, has a high rainfall and a shorter growing season.

Soils

The soils of Great Britain are extremely varied. Poor thin soils are found in large areas of Scotland, Northern Ireland, Wales and in the Pennines, the Lake District, Exmoor and Dartmoor. The majority of farms in these areas carry only hardy single suckling beef herds and flocks of hill sheep.

In the lowlands, however, some of the most fertile soil in the world is to be found. Parts of Herefordshire, Worcestershire and Kent are renowned for their fertility; crops like hops and market garden crops are grown for these require very fertile soil and copious amounts of farmyard manure.

The midland counties of Northamptonshire, Leicestershire and South Shropshire possess some very fine fattening pastures. In the eastern counties, where much of the land is level, fertile and with a low rainfall, mainly arable crops are grown.

Farming systems

If we divide the country into three, by drawing two imaginary lines from north to south (see Fig. 15), we can see the main farming pattern. The western area is predominantly stockrearing, the midlands growing and grass fattening, the eastern counties mainly arable. The arable farmer imports cattle from the north and west for yard fattening during the winter months.

Stockrearing

Hill farms

Most of the commercial livestock rearing farms are found in the hill, upland and marginal areas. Much of the farmland is classified as rough grazing, and consists of open hill, moors, peat bog and open heath. Because of the severe climatic conditions in these parts, only hardy beef cows capable of breeding and suckling one calf per year are kept. Sheep form the main farm enterprise as they are hardier than cattle, and able to forage for most of the year.

Marginal farms

Marginal farms are located in areas lying between the hills and lowlands. The land is more productive than the hill farm, but substantially poorer than the lowland farms. This means that any improvement to the farm in the way of ploughing, reseeding, liming and drainage, will carry the same high costs as a lowland farm, but the returns from crops, increased stocking and better quality stock will not be in the same proportion as would be found in the lowlands, owing to the low inherent fertility of the soil. In other words it is 'marginal'.

Good examples of marginal farms are to be found along the border counties of Scotland and Wales. Beef calves are reared on single suckling and multiple suckling systems. After weaning, the calves are run on to the yearling stage and then sold for finishing in the lowlands.

Grassland fattening

Grass is the cheapest food produced on the farm and, if properly utilized, can be one of the less expensive means of fattening cattle. Traditionally, grassland farmers purchase well grown store cattle in the spring and feed them through the grazing season. This often leads to an over-supply of finished cattle in late summer and early autumn, and consequently a drop in prices.

The secret of profitable summer feeding seems to be in skilful buying of suitable stock early in the year before the grazing season starts when prices are relatively low, followed by rapid feeding so as to market the finished beast in late July before the autumn glut of cattle lowers the market price.

Arable fattening

Until quite recently, beef cattle were kept on the arable farms for the sole purpose of converting cheap arable by-products into farm-yard manure for growing cash crops. It may still be worthwhile keeping cattle for this purpose but most farmers today look for a profit from their beef cattle as well.

Yard fattening is much more expensive than grass fattening, but fortunately yard finished cattle are marketed at the higher winter prices. A further reason for having beef cattle on the arable farm is that they find profitable work for the men during the slack winter months.

Intensive beef production

We have seen so far in this chapter that traditionally the beef animal is raised in three stages – calf rearing, store period and the final fattening. This may mean that the finished animal has been kept by three, or possibly four farmers, each of whom will expect to make a small profit. In more recent years we have however witnessed a tremendous change in beef production. Many lowland farmers now breed, or buy in, dairy bred calves, such as the pure-bred Friesian, and rear them from the calf stage through to the finished animal. Some farmers will rear up to ten calves on a nurse cow during her lactation (multiple suckling) and then fatten them at around 15–20 months old on grass, or with the use of supplementary concentrates.

Other farmers adopt what is known as the 'barley beef' system whereby pure-bred dairy bull calves (except Jersey and Guernsey) are reared artificially on a milk replacement, and then grown on and finally fattened on an all-concentrate diet of barley meal mixed with some protein, vitamins and minerals. Barley beeves are kept indoors throughout their lives and are marketed when they weigh approximately 400–500 kg live-weight at about 12 months old.

Chapter Six
Breeds of Cattle

Beef breeds

Hereford

Named after its county of origin, this is numerically the most important breed in the world. It is easily recognized by its white face and deep red coat, with occasionally white markings over the crest, brisket, belly and legs. The 'white face' is a dominant characteristic which means that when Hereford cattle are mated to other breeds, the offspring always have white faces. This is known as colour marking. In size, the Hereford is larger than the Aberdeen Angus, mature cows weighing around 500–550 kg. A notable feature of the breed is its ability to grow quickly, especially when at grass. Calves will grow at 1 kg or more daily, if well fed, and reach maturity in 18–20 months. Herefords are extremely hardy and excellent grazers.

Hereford bulls are widely used for crossing with dual-purpose breeds to produce beef from a dairy herd. The Hereford and Friesian makes a most acceptable beef animal. It grows quickly, produces a first class carcass, covered with firm fat, and has little wastage in the dressing owing to the thin black hide, as compared with the pure Hereford. Butchers prefer the Hereford × Friesian to the pure-bred Hereford.

An interesting point is that the Hereford produces a yellow fat which, it is claimed, enables the breed to withstand extremes of temperature. This may be one of the reasons for the breed's outstanding popularity overseas.

Without doubt, the Hereford is a very handsome, rugged breed with tremendous constitution.

Polled Herefords

These have been bred in America since 1889. A Polled Register was established in 1902 and this is known as the American Polled Hereford Breeders Association II.

In England, polled breeding began in 1949, when a group of breeders formed the British Polled Breeders Association. This society used the Galloway bull to gain poll characteristics whilst retaining the red coat. After four generations from the original cross the bulls are accepted as pure polls.

Aberdeen Angus

The Aberdeen Angus originated on the east coast of Scotland around the counties of Angus and Aberdeen. The cattle are naturally polled and have black coats with occasional small white patches on the belly and flanks. Both polling and the black coat are dominant characteristics when the breed is crossed with other cattle. In size the Aberdeen Angus is one of the smaller beef breeds, mature cows weighing around 450 kg live-weight. The cattle are hardy and have a robust constitution.

Although they are excellent grazers, we usually associate the breed with yard fattening in the seed potato growing areas of East Scotland and East Anglia. The two systems are complementary for the yarded cattle make copious amounts of F.Y.M. for the root crops.

The Angus has a world-wide reputation for producing superb quality beef. It yields a deeply fleshed carcass full of lean meat, with a minimum amount of bone, and a smooth covering of white firm fat. The secondary offals – head, hide, feet, etc. – are small in comparison with the body so that the beast has a high dressing percentage, or carcass yield. The only disadvantage of the breed is that compared with the Charolais or Hereford it tends to grow rather slowly.

For many years the Angus cow has been crossed with a white Shorthorn beef bull to produce the well known colour-marked Blue Greys, a cross-breed that is very popular with both farmers and butchers.

The Angus bull is used widely on dairy cows, particularly Friesian heifers, for not only does it sire high quality beef calves, but the heifers have less difficulty at calving than mated to the Friesian bull. This is due to the smaller head and shoulders of the Angus-cross calf.

Beef Shorthorn

Beef Shorthorn or Scots Shorthorn is known generally as the 'Great Improver' for without doubt it is one of the world's finest beef breeds. It originated from the early 'Teeswater' cattle found in Northern England but has been improved in Scotland. The cattle may be white, red or roan in colour.

Unfortunately they are not 'colour marking' but their progeny are easily recognized by cattlemen by the blocky appearance and the stamp of quality in the calves.

The beefing characteristics are excellent for the animals are short-legged, thick set and carry a wealth of deep flesh over the loin and hind quarters. Like the Angus there is little wastage in hides, or other secondary offal at slaughter.

The bulls are now widely mated with Ayrshire cows as well as with Friesian and Dairy Shorthorns to produce more beef from the dairy herd. The White Shorthorn bull is crossed with either the Aberdeen Angus, Galloway or Highland cow to produce the popular Blue Greys.

Lincoln Reds

These are descended from the early Shorthorn (Teeswater) cattle and were formerly dual-purpose. The present-day breed is an extreme beef type, early maturing and capable of rapid growth. The cattle are excellent grazers and are found throughout the Midland grazing areas.

The cattle are red in colour and horned, although recently a polled strain has been introduced.

Devon

Devon cattle, usually referred to as 'Red Rubies', because of their deep red coat, tend to be rather a localized breed, found mainly in South-West England. The cows weigh around 550–600 kg and calves will easily put 1 kg live-weight on a day. The cattle are noted grazers and thrive readily on the open hills of 'Glorious Devon'.

Galloway

Galloway cattle are similar in appearance and size to the Aberdeen Angus except that they have thick curly black, grey or dun coats. The breed is exceptionally hardy and able to thrive in the most exposed areas of Scotland.

Under favourable conditions the cattle will fatten, perhaps a little slowly, to produce excellent quality beef.

Galloway cows are mated to a white Shorthorn bull to produce the Blue Grey.

Belted Galloway

These are similar to the Galloway except that they have a white band running round the body.

Highland

Highland cattle are the hardiest breed found in Great Britain. They live mainly in the exposed areas of Northern Scotland. The breed is famous for its long horns and shaggy coat which may be dun, reddish brown or brindle in colour.

The cattle are slow to mature but produce fine-grained lean meat. Like the Galloway and Angus the cows may be mated to a white Shorthorn bull to breed Blue Greys.

Welsh Black

Welsh Black cattle originated in the Snowdonia region of North Wales where they are mainly found today. The cattle are all black and horned, very hardy and well able to withstand the high rainfall of North Wales. The breed is often crossed with the Galloway to produce a polled cross-bred that is extremely hardy.

More common is the Hereford × Welsh Black which makes an ideal thrifty grazing animal for fattening in the Welsh valleys and lowlands.

Sussex

This is a fairly localized breed, found mainly in South-East England.

It is characterized by its deep cherry red coat. Mature cows weigh around 600 kg and have the reputation for being good mothers, weaning strong calves even when they are grazed on poor pastures. The breed is popular in South Africa because of its ability to withstand wide changes of temperature.

Dual-purpose breeds

British Friesian

British Friesian, usually referred to as Black and Whites, produce approximately 80 per cent of our milk supplies and 60 per cent of our home produced beef. Undoubtedly the British Friesian is the most important breed of cattle in Great Britain; to quote the British Friesian Cattle Society, the breed is 'single purpose with dual results'!

Beef characteristics

The pure-bred Friesian steer has the ability to grow quickly, convert food efficiently and produce a well finished, lean carcass. To do this, it is important to feed steers adequately at all stages of growth, avoiding checks and a store period. Failure to do this will result in leggy, coarse boned animals which may take an extra 12 months to fatten and result in heavy half-fat steers of 600–650 kg that will not suit the present-day consumer demand.

The Friesian steer is ideally suited to intensive, indoor feeding systems such as barley beef. In this case a steer may be expected to average a daily live-weight gain of 1 kg and be fit for slaughter when 12–13 months old.

The Angus or Hereford × Friesian makes an ideal grazing or yard feeding beast which will reach maturity at 20–24 months, weighing around 500–550 kg. Mature Friesian cows weigh around 550–600 kg.

Dairy Shorthorn

The Dairy Shorthorn is one of the oldest breeds originating in the Valley of the Tees, near Durham where it was developed from the Teeswater cattle. At one time it was numerically the most important breed in England, but in recent years has given way to the Friesian.

Pure-bred Shorthorns produce satisfactory beef but they are at their best when crossed with the Hereford Bull; indeed it would be difficult to find a better all round beef animal than the Hereford × Shorthorn.

The cows are docile, hardy and easy to manage. They are popular on marginal farms where a rugged, deep milking cow is required for multiple suckling and producing milk for the household.

Dairy Shorthorn may be red, white or roan in colour, the cows weighing around 500–550 kg.

Red Poll

This is an outstanding example of a dual-purpose breed. The bull calves and surplus heifers make excellent beef and the cows are exceptionally fine milkers.

Fattening stock are good grazers but also respond to yard feeding. The breed has done very well in carcass competitions.

South Devon

The South Devon is our largest breed, mature cows weighing 650–700 kg and bulls often weighing a tonne or more. The cattle are horned and have a light brown-red coat. The cows produce high quality milk which attracts the same premium as Channel Island milk.

Like the Devon (Red Rubies) the breed tends to be confined to its native county and Cornwall.

Dairy breeds

Ayrshire

This is a pure dairy breed which until recently was thought to be unsuitable for beef production. However, many farmers now cross their lower yielding cows with a Beef Shorthorn or Charolais bull to produce cross-breds that are suitable for intensive or semi-intensive systems.

Channel Island

Jersey and Guernsey cattle, known as the Channel Island breeds,

64

are pure dairy cattle and generally regarded as unsuitable for commercial beef production. However, some breeders have used the Charolais bull for crossing and have been pleased with the results, but this is by no means general.

Chapter Seven
Other European Breeds

Charolais

This is the most important breed in France. The breed originated in the old province of Charollais, but it is now widely dispersed throughout the world. The cattle are noted for their rapid growth rate, size and the high proportion of lean meat that is produced on the hind quarters. They are creamy-white, horned and have rounded hind quarters rather than square and blocky. Mature cows weigh around 700–750 kg and bulls often reach a tonne or more. Calves are capable of a 1–1·5 kg daily live-weight gain.

In 1961, thirty-one young Charolais bulls were imported from France by the Ministry of Agriculture for trial crossing with British cattle. The bulls were placed at A.I. centres and their resulting progeny were very carefully assessed. The results were later published by the Milk Marketing Board in *The Charolais Report* (see page 72). The Report showed quite clearly that the Charolais bull could be used with advantage on dairy cows to produce good quality beef. It also revealed that cows carried their calves in uterus for up to three days longer than similar Hereford cross calves and not surprisingly were up to 4 kg heavier at birth.

Today the Charolais is used extensively on dairy and beef breeds to produce excellent quality lean meat. Charolais females have now been imported and many pedigree herds of Charolais cattle established.

Simmental

The Simmental originated in the Simme Valley in Switzerland from which it gets its name. From there it has been exported to many countries to upgrade local cattle.

There are now four main types of Simmental: the original

Swiss Simmental; the Austrian Simmental; the German Fleckvich and the Pie-Rouge de l'est in France. The total population is around 35 million and is, numerically, the most important dual-purpose breed in Europe.

The Simmental has a white face, rather similar to the Hereford's, which is colour marking. Its coat colour is yellowish brown or red combined with characteristic white markings. There is frequently a white stripe on the shoulder and further white markings on the loin, belly, legs and tail. Bulls weigh around a tonne and cows about 700–750 kg.

Although the Simmental is dual-purpose, it was introduced into the United Kingdom mainly for its beef characteristics. Subsequently, however, many breeders have found the value of Simmental cross cows for suckler herds, where their milking ability is invaluable in rearing suckled calves.

Milk production figures for various types of Simmental

	Yield in kg	Butterfat
Swiss Simmental	4091	3·91
Austrian Simmental	4483	4·13
German Simmental	3921	3·98
French Simmental	3900	3·80

Source: Milk Marketing Board, *Better Breeding*.

From these figures it would appear that the Austrian and Swiss cattle are the best milkers, but it should be remembered that the management and land between countries vary enormously and this may tend to conceal any real genetic difference between them.

The Simmental has been introduced into Britain for its beef characteristics and there is no doubt that it is an excellent beef breed.

Limousin

The Limousin breed originates from the province of Limousin in west-central France. It is a very old breed and is second to the Charolais in importance in France.

The Limousin has a rich golden red coloured coat which shades to a lighter tan under the belly and around the legs. In size the breed is smaller than the Charolais and Simmental; mature bulls weigh around a tonne and cows about 600 kg. Pure-bred Limousins tend to produce light-weight calves of between 35–40 kg and the French claim that the cows have easy calvings.

French breed birth weights (to nearest 0·5 kg)

Breed	Males	Females
Limousin	39 kg	36·5 kg
Charolais	45·5 kg	42 kg
Blonde d'Aquitaine	47·0 kg	43 kg
Maine Anjou	50·5 kg	48 kg

The Limousin produces a most acceptable carcass with a high proportion of lean meat to bone and fat. If fed on a high plane of nutrition the cattle may be sold for slaughter at practically any age – either as three-month-old veal or after two seasons at grass as heavyweights of around 550 kg.

Maine Anjou

The Maine Anjou has evolved in the east of Brittany in France from a cross between the Durham and the local Mancelle cattle. The Maine Anjou Cattle Society was founded in 1908 and they have since selected the breed for increased body size and milk production. Today, the cattle are some of the largest in Europe. Although claimed by the Breed Society to be dual-purpose the beefing characteristics far exceed the milking ability.

The coat colour is mainly red and a little white with patches of roan on some animals. The cattle have big frames and carry well-muscled shoulders and a long muscular rump with deep flesh carried down on the thighs. The breed will certainly grow and finish rapidly, finally producing a carcass of excellent quality.

The first importation to Britain of Maine Anjou was in 1972.

Blonde d'Aquitaine

The Blonde d'Aquitaine is descended from the old Garonne breed and has subsequently been improved by introducing Limousin and English Beef Shorthorn blood.

Later these cattle were combined with the Pyrenean Blond to form the Blonde d'Aquitaine Herd Book. This diverse system of breeding has led to a wide variation in breed type. However, French breeders are participating in an intensive breeding programme to unify the breed into one type embodying all the best characteristics of the component breeds.

The Blonde d'Aquitaine is light fawn in colour although the legs tend to be a slightly lighter shade from the rest of the body. The head is of medium length and narrow with a broad poll.

The cattle have a strongly muscled body, are wide in the hips, rounded behind and good throughout the hind quarters.

The Blonde d'Aquitaine is essentially a beef breed and has little milk potential. In trials the breed has shown exceptionally good food conversion and produces a good carcass with little fat.

Meuse-Rhine-Issel

The Meuse-Rhine-Issel breed originated in the south and southeastern regions of the Netherlands in the districts bordering the great Dutch rivers, the Meuse, the Rhine and the Issel, from which it gains its name.

The breed is descended from the Dutch Friesian but differs in colour and size, being red and white in colour and having more beef characteristics than the Friesian.

The M-R-I calves are ideal for Dutch veal production being, on average, 2 kg heavier than similar Friesian calves at birth and capable of rapid growth when fed high-energy liquid diets.

Specially formulated milk replacement feeds are available and under ideal management calves weigh 150 kg in about 4 months when they are slaughtered.

When kept under traditional systems the calves grow very similarly to the British Friesian. M-R-I cows are kept mainly for milk production and again their yield is similar to the Friesian.

The M-R-I breed was first imported into the UK in 1970.

Chianina

The Chianina, pronounced Key-a-neena, is claimed to be the largest breed of cattle in the world. Mature bulls weigh over $1\frac{1}{2}$ tonnes and stand upwards of 2 m high! Many have shown liveweight gains of 2 kg per day.

The Chianina is a native of Northern Italy where they have been kept for milk and beef production and also used as draught animals.

Maine Anjou

Charolais

Limousin

Marchigiana

Simmental

Chianna

The coat colour is white, but exposed skin areas are black. The eyelids, switch and hooves are also black. Calves, however, are born a tan colour which gradually turns white when they are 8–10 weeks old.

Despite their enormous size, Chianinas are extremely docile and easy to handle. At birth bull calves weigh around 45 kg and heifers 38 kg. This is a comparatively light birth weight and so there should be little difficulty in calving.

The breed was first introduced into the UK in 1972 by means of importing Chianina semen from Italy. This was followed later by live cattle imports.

Brown Swiss (Braunvich)

The Brown Swiss is one of the oldest breeds in Europe and has been bred pure for over 1000 years. It is a medium size breed and kept for both meat and milk production. In colour the coat is beige-brown, varying in tone from lighter coloured areas around the legs, muzzle and ears. It has white coloured horns with black tips.

Kept under favourable lowland conditions the breed average for milk production in recorded herds is around 3900 kg at 3·89 per cent butterfat. Cows are renowned for their longevity and many breed regularly for upwards of twelve lactations.

The breed has excellent beef potential. In feeding trials daily gains of 1·45–1·77 kg have been recorded on intensive systems, whilst with average management about 1 kg is normal.

The breed is early maturing and therefore produces lighter carcasses than the Simmental.

German Yellow (Gelbvieh)

The Gelbvieh breed is found in the lower central area of Germany where farms in general tend to be small in size and carry relatively small herds. The breed was developed from local cattle but improvements were later made by introducing Simmental and Brown Swiss blood lines.

The coat colour varies from cream to reddish-yellow. The breed is dual-purpose and the average yield for all recorded cows in

Fig. 16 (opposite) European breeds of bull

Bavaria in 1972 was 3634 kg at 4·03 per cent butterfat. Calving difficulties, it is claimed, are rare.

The Gelbvieh beef animal tends to grow rather more slowly and produce a lighter carcass than the Simmental but, nevertheless, is an extremely useful beef animal.

Murray Grey

The Murray Grey was developed initially in Australia, by crossing an Aberdeen Angus bull on a very light roan Shorthorn cow. For the next forty years only Angus bulls were used on the grey cattle but the grey colour persisted.

In 1965 the first volume of the Murray Grey Herdbook was published and the breed is now well established in Australia.

The breed possesses the best characteristics of the Angus and Shorthorn. It is fine-boned and has exceptional fleshing qualities with good marbling.

Murray Greys have recently been imported into Britain and semen is obtainable through A.I.

References

Better Breeding – Beef Breeds Special, P. Tyler, Milk Marketing Board, Surrey, 1975.

Report No. 29, Beef Improvement Services, Meat and Livestock Commission.

Preliminary Report, Germ Plasm Evaluation Program, US Meat and Animal Research Center.

European Breeds of Cattle, vols. 1 and 2, FAO, 1966.

Comparative Beef Breeds Performance of the Large Cattle Breeds of Western Europe, I. L. Mason.

Reprint No. 88, Commonwealth Bureau of Animal Breeding and Genetics.

The Charolais Report, J. Edwards, D. Jobst, J. Hodges, M. Leyburn, L. K. O'Connor, A. McDonald, G. F. Smith and P. Wood, Milk Marketing Board, 1966.

Chapter Eight
Stockrearing

'Bucket' feeding

'Bucket' rearing is a system that uses a manufactured milk replacement to rear calves instead of feeding whole milk.

It includes feeding calves from nipple drinkers, automatic dispensing machines, early weaning, and twelve-week weaning.

Generally speaking, we find 'bucket' rearing on farms in lowland areas where land is too expensive to justify keeping nurse cows. Provided that the farm has good buildings, quite an intensive beef unit can be established on a relatively small acreage by purchasing calves and rearing them indoors with a suitable milk substitute. The success of the enterprise will largely depend upon the skill of the person in charge of the unit. Close attention to detail, scrupulously clean feeding utensils, regular feeding times and a watchful eye for calf ailments and diseases are all part of the stockrearer's responsibility.

Fig. 17 'Bucket' feeding

Calves suitable for beef production

The most popular calves for rearing are the colour-marked Aberdeen Angus, Hereford and Charolais, crossed with dairy breeds.

However, any of the pure-bred beef breeds, or their crosses with selected dairy herds, are suitable for beef production.

When selecting rearing calves, look for healthy, vigorous, well made animals that show plenty of bone and substance. An alert appearance, bright bold eye, and glossy coat are indications of a healthy calf. Place your hand over the calf's shoulder blade; if three fingers can span the shoulder, it is a reasonable indication that the calf will develop a beef conformation. Narrow shoulders suggest a high proportion of dairy blood, and the resulting animal is likely to have angular, dairy-like characteristics.

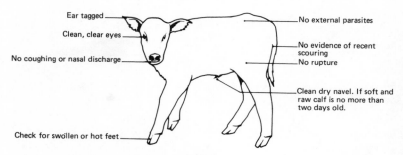

Fig. 18 Calf suitable for beef production

Bought-in calves

Calves purchased in markets, or directly from other farms, require particularly careful attention during their first two weeks. On arrival the calves should be housed singly in warm draught-free pens. During cold or damp weather it will be an advantage to hang an infra-red lamp over the new arrivals for the first few days to avoid chills and make the calf feel comfortable.

Bought-in calves should only be fed 1 litre of warm water with two tablespoonfuls of glucose added, for the first one or two feeds. This will allow the stomach to settle down and help to avoid digestive scours. If the farm has a recent history of white scours (see page oo) then veterinary advice should be sought. The veterinary surgeon will be able to give an anti-serum injection or prescribe

74

an antibiotic feed that will give the calf immunity to the bacteria causing the infection. Scouring is quite common with purchased calves and is often due to the calf not receiving sufficient colostrum from its dam before it was sold or being affected by a chill on the journey to the farm.

Value of colostrum

Colostrum, sometimes called 'beastings', is secreted by the cow during the first three to four days after calving. Colostrum has a higher feeding value than ordinary milk and it contains antibodies which protect the calf from disease. It is rich in vitamins A and D and also has a laxative effect on the digestive system. This helps to remove the meconium or foetal dung. Ideally, calves should be allowed to suckle their dams for the first three days. If they are removed at birth it is essential that the colostrum is 'bucket' fed to the calf at blood temperature (37·5–38°C).

Colostrum substitute

If a cow dies at calving, or for some reason fails to produce colostrum, then an effort should be made to obtain either some surplus beastings or to feed a colostrum substitute.

A well known recipe is to whip up a fresh raw egg in 1 litre of milk and add half a litre of boiled water, 1 teaspoonful cod liver oil and 1 dessertspoon of castor oil. This is sufficient for one feed and should be fed at blood temperature, three times a day for the first three days. Once the black jelly-like foetal dung is passed, then the castor oil can be omitted.

Fig. 19 (a) Teaching a calf to drink

Teaching a calf to drink

Stand the calf with its tail in a corner of the pen; this gives you better control. Hold the bucket in one hand at knee height. Place your arm around the calf's neck, then gently insert two fingers into the mouth. Once the calf begins to suck, lower the head into the bucket. As the calf sucks your fingers it will draw milk into its mouth. After two or three meals the calf will probably drink naturally without the aid of your fingers.

Early weaning calf rearing system

The early weaning system is now accepted by the majority of farmers who use milk substitute as being the most satisfactory method of rearing. The calves are weaned off milk replacement on to solid food when three to five weeks old. Whilst some rearers find three-week weaning satisfactory, five-week weaning is, perhaps, a safer method; but on no account should calves be weaned if they are not eating plenty of the dry food mentioned in the guide below.

Calves bought-in are best treated as though they were born on the day of arrival; and should be weaned five weeks after arrival and not when they are estimated to be five weeks old.

The main advantage of the early weaning system is that by encouraging the calf to eat solid food at a few days old the rumen will develop at an earlier age. Once cudding begins, the calf is much better able to overcome digestive troubles, and the risk of scours is reduced. Early weaning also demands considerably less labour than the old twelve-week rearing system.

Early weaning guide

1–4 days	Allow the calf to suckle dam, or feed 3 litres of colostrum per day in 3 feeds.
5–10 days	3 litres milk daily, gradually replacing the milk with a proprietary milk replacement. The milk powder should be whisked into warm water. Clean utensils thoroughly after each feed. If possible feed three times per day.
	Introduce some proprietary baby calf pencils by placing a handful in the bottom of the bucket after

	each feed. Clean, fresh water must be provided and a little soft, good quality hay offered.
11–28 days	Increase the milk replacement to 4 litres per day, fed in two feeds.
	Baby calf pencils should be freely available, together with clean water and fresh hay.
29–35 days	Reduce the milk replacement by $\frac{1}{2}$ litre per day, weaning the calf on the 35th day. Make sure that the calf is eating at least 0·5 kg of calf pencils daily.

Once per day feeding

This system requires the use of specially formulated milk powders which usually have a high fat content. The manufacturers claim that by including animal fats such as beef dripping in the formulation of their product, they can produce a milk replacement that is equally as nutritious as whole milk.

High fat powder is mixed at the rate of 425 g in 3 litres of warm water and fed to the calves once per day from about the third day onwards. Depending upon the size, health and general well-being of the calf the daily allowance should start at around 2–2·5 litres per day, increasing to 3 litres when 7–10 days old.

Water, good hay and concentrates should be made available as in twice a day feeding and the calf is similarly weaned by gradually reducing the liquid feed from the 30th day onwards. Final weaning takes place on the 35th day.

This system is now widely adopted by farmers rearing dairy heifers and is gradually gaining favour with beef producers too. The main advantage is the considerable saving in labour for preparation of liquid feed and washing up utensils take considerable time. Also, with once a day feeding you may feed at any specified hour – say immediately after the stockman has had breakfast, but it is important that the same time is used each day.

However, if this system is adopted it is most important that the calves are inspected at least twice daily to make sure that they are fit and well.

Machine feeders

There are several excellent machines available to farmers which automatically prepare and dispense milk substitute to calves.

Such machines warm the water and mix in the powder to a specified concentration and dispense the liquid through one or more teats. Some machines pump the feed to calves housed singly, whilst other systems allow groups of up to fifteen calves to use one central teat.

With constant access to the teat each calf is able to obtain an adequate amount but quite often one finds 'boss' calves standing by the teat and thus preventing more nervous animals from taking sufficient food. This can, in some instances, affect the subsequent growth rate of the poorer calf, but, in general, very good results are found with these machines.

There is, of course, considerable saving in labour, but great care is needed to wash and maintain the machine in proper order.

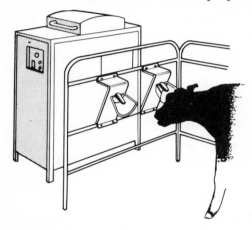

Fig. 19 (b)   Automatic dispensing machine

Ten tips for successful calf rearing

Calves must receive adequate colostrum.
Read the instructions carefully before mixing the milk replacement.
Clean utensils thoroughly after use.
Feed at regular hours.
Have an infra-red lamp available for ailing calves.
Clean, fresh water must always be available.
Offer fresh concentrates daily.
Bed calves with clean wheat straw daily.
Soft meadow hay is preferable to seed hay.

Pens should be thoroughly cleansed using hot water and washing soda after each batch of calves. Resting pens for 1 month will lower the risk of disease.

Chapter Nine
Stockman's Skills

Castration

Bull calves intended for traditional beef production should be castrated before they are three months old. Once castrated the calf is called a steer or bullock. Castration prevents breeding and improves carcass quality. The operation may be performed either surgically using a castrating knife or scalpel, bloodlessly with the use of a Burdizzo instrument, or by the rubber ring and elastrator.

Surgical castration

Surgical castration should only be performed by a veterinary surgeon or persons who have received instruction from a qualified teacher of stockman's tasks. The operation requires a high degree of skill and strict observance of hygiene.

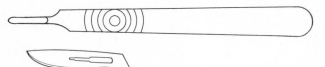

Fig. 20 (a) Surgical scalpel with detachable blade suitable for castrating

Equipment Sterile sharp castrating knife or scalpel, cotton wool, hot water, soap, antiseptic wash, sulphanilamide powder, halter.

The calf should be haltered and left standing for the operation.

Procedure
Wash hands and arms thoroughly.
Wash calf's scrotum with warm water and mild antiseptic.
Grasp the scrotum with left hand.

Make incision down the right-hand side of scrotum to expose testicle.

Withdraw testicle and carefully scrape tissue around spermatic cord.

Remove testicle either by gentle traction or by cutting the cord with scalpel.

Complete second testicle.

Dust the open wounds with sulphanilamide powder.

Return calf to a clean, well strawed pen.

Bloodless castration

The calf may be cast or left standing for bloodless castration. A special instrument invented by Dr Burdizzo of Italy is used. Burdizzo instruments are marketed in three sizes: small, medium and large. The medium size is best suited for small calves.

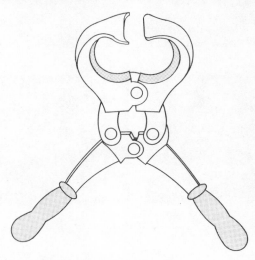

Fig. 20 (b)   Burdizzo bloodless castrator

Equipment   Bloodless castrator, sulphanilamide powder, halter.

Procedure

Hold the Burdizzo with jaws open in right hand.

Grasp the testicle with left hand and gently pull downwards.

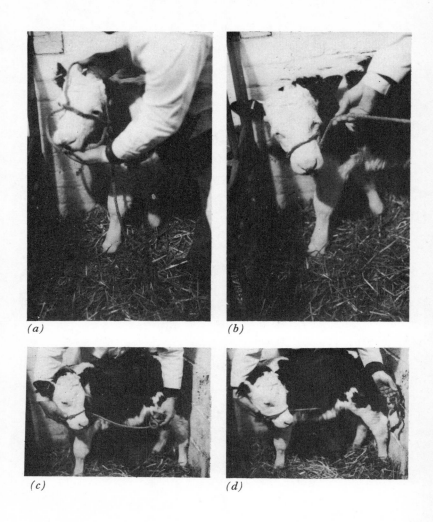

(a) (b)

(c) (d)

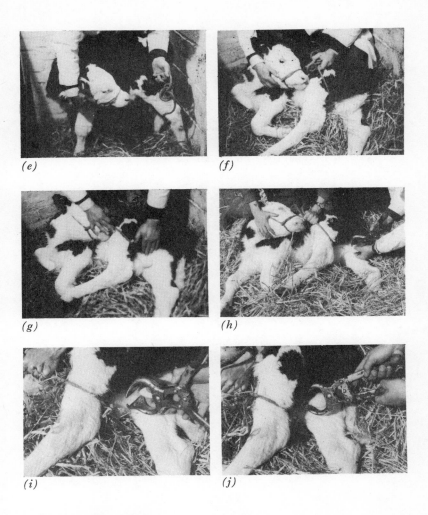

Fig. 21 (a)   Haltering calf
       (b)
       (c)   Using halter to cast a calf
       (d)   Slip end of cord around hind legs
       (e)
       (f)   Calf restrained
       (g)   Scrotum exposed
       (h)   Burdizzo castrator
       (i)   Spermatic cord in jaws
       (j)   Castration completed

Place the Burdizzo over spermatic cord and close the jaws partly when you are quite certain that the cord is firmly fixed in the instrument. Complete castration by fully closing both jaws.

Keep the castrator in closed position for 15–20 seconds, then release.

Proceed with second testicle, making the crush slightly above or below first mark. This will allow the blood to circulate to the purse although both spermatic cords have been crushed.

Dust the bruised skin with sulphanilamide powder.

With strong calves it may be necessary to pinch each cord twice, but generally one crush will give satisfactory results.

There may be a slight swelling for a few days after castration.

Elastrator and rubber rings

It is best to cast the calf for this task.

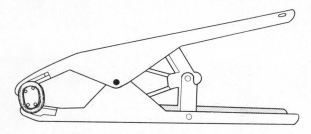

Fig. 22　Elastrator with rubber ring fitted ready for expansion

Procedure

Halter calf, run the cord between calf's hind legs, then cast the calf by pulling cord.

Assistant holds calf in lying position by maintaining traction on halter.

Place ring over the scrotum. Be careful not to release ring until you are quite sure that both testicles are down.

Check that the ring will not pinch the belly skin, or include the supernumerary teats.

Release ring into position by withdrawing the elastrator.

The ring must be applied before the calf is 7 days old. The entire scrotum and testicles will drop off in 10–14 days.

Disbudding

The electric cauterizer is the most widely used instrument for disbudding although gas heated cauterizers are available and perfectly satisfactory. The hot iron method is used with calves three to four weeks old. A local anaesthetic must be used.

Equipment   Hot iron cauterizer, hypodermic syringe, 2 × 10 mm 18 gauge needles, local anaesthetic, cotton wool, surgical spirit, pair curved blade scissors.

Use of local anaesthetic   A suitable local anaesthetic such as lignocaine hydrochloride should be obtained from a veterinary surgeon. The student must also seek advice from a veterinary surgeon or qualified teacher in veterinary tasks as to dose rate and the exact size of injection.

Procedure

Plug in electric cauterizer; make sure plug has an effective earth. Irons usually require 15–20 minutes to heat up.

Swab cornea nerve area with surgical spirit.

Inject 2 cc local anaesthetic per horn bud into the cornea nerve area. The cornea nerve may be found by running a finger above the eyelid towards the forehead. A slight hollow will be found. See Fig. 23 (c).

Allow ten minutes for the anaesthetic to take effect.

Clip the hair from around the horn buds; this makes it easier to see where the hot iron is to be placed.

Lightly tap the horn bud or prick with a hypodermic needle, carefully watching the reflex action to ensure that the anaesthetic has taken effect.

Test the hot iron to see that it is sufficiently hot by applying the tip to a piece of wood. If the iron burns the wood it is ready for disbudding.

Either halter the calf's head securely to a post or ask an assistant to hold the head steady by placing one hand under the jaw and with the second hand holding the calf's ear flat against his head.

Place the iron over the exposed horn bud and apply gentle pressure, twisting the iron with the wrist to give a cutting effect. After 10–15 seconds the horn bud may be gouged out, leaving a clean even depth ring of seared tissue.

The cavity may be left or dusted with a little sulphanilamide powder.

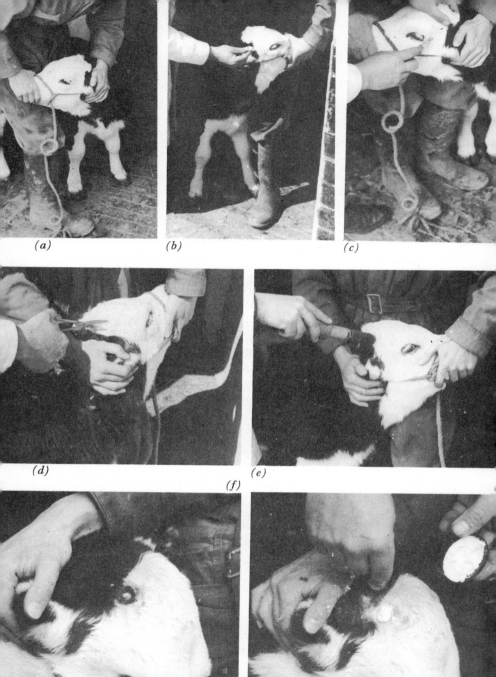

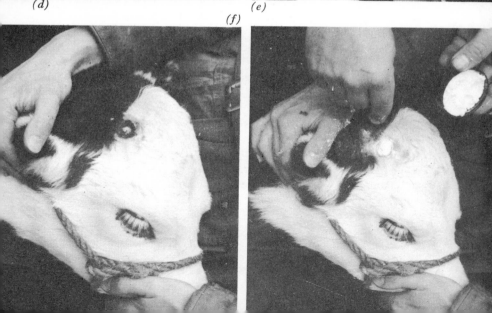

Ear tags

All calves must be ear marked to conform with the Attested Herd Regulations.

Ear tags are now approved by the Ministry of Agriculture under the Tuberculosis Order 1964.

The tag has the herd number on the female side and the calf's individual number on the male side.

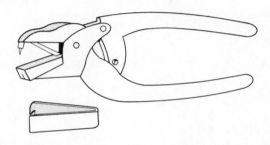

Fig. 24 (a)   Ear tag with forceps

The tag is inserted in the top side of the right ear, close to the head. Fig. 24 (b).

Procedure

Restrain calf either by haltering or standing it in the corner of a pen.

Place tag in applicators.

Insert tag in right ear, allow 10 mm space between ear and tip of tag to allow for the ear to grow. Avoid damaging the artery and veins.

Fig. 23 (a)   Calf held securely
  (b)   Swab area around cornea nerve with surgical spirit
  (c)   Injection of local anaesthetic
  (d)   Cut hair away from horn buds
  (e)   Apply hot iron to horn bud
  (f)   Clean brown ring of seared tissue
  (g)   Dust cavity with antiseptic powder

Veterinary Surgeons Act 1966

The first paragraph is the same as that in Part I of the first schedule to the 1948 Act, i.e. it permits any *treatment* given to an animal by its owner, by another member of the owner's household, or by a person in the employment of the owner.

Certain minor operations may be performed by people over the age of eighteen. The operations are as follows:

(a) Castration of calves and lambs; caponizing, whether by chemical means or otherwise.

(b) Tailing of a lamb.

(c) Docking of the tail of a dog before its eyes are open.

Part II of schedule 3 prohibits the castration by an unqualified person of a horse, pony, ass or mule, of a bull which has reached the age of 12 months, of a goat, ram, boar, cat or dog which has reached the age of 6 months.

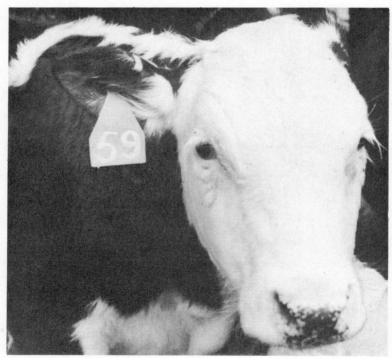

Fig. 24 (b)   Ear tag in position

Protection of Animals (Anaesthetics) Acts 1954 and 1964

Rubber rings must be applied to ram lambs and bull calves before they are 7 days old.

Local anaesthetics must be used for castration either surgically or when using a Burdizzo on calves and lambs over 3 months old.

Local anaesthetics must be used for disbudding calves with a hot iron.

Chapter Ten
The Management of Suckler Herds

Single suckling is undoubtedly the best way to rear strong, healthy calves. The only disadvantage is the high cost of purchasing and maintaining a cow solely to breed and rear one calf per year.

However, the system is justified on hill, upland and marginal farms where the land is poor, and climatic conditions often severe; on some lowland arable farms where a low labour cost enterprise is required; and in valuable pedigree herds where the aim is to produce breeding stock for sale at above commercial prices.

The upland herd

The cow

The choice of breed is largely dependent upon the district in which the cow is to live. The small beef breeds are hardier and require less food for maintenance than the larger breeds, but they do not grow as fast, nor milk as well as big cattle.

Whatever the final choice is, it is important that the cows are of good 'breed type', healthy, hardy and rugged. They must be capable of breeding regularly, bearing strong healthy calves and producing some 1000 to 1500 litres of milk in a six to eight month lactation.

With these qualities the majority of suckler cows will breed regularly for eight to ten years; many will go on breeding much longer than this.

The bull

There is much truth in the old saying that the bull is half the herd. One could say that the influence of the sire in a suckled herd can mean the difference between profit and loss.

Apart from getting the cows quickly in calf, the bull must transmit 'quality' and a capacity to grow quickly to his calves.

Matched lots of blocky, thick set, well grown, weaned calves will command high prices at suckler calf sales, while plain, long-legged, shelly calves will barely make enough to cover the cost of rearing. Good bulls are always difficult to find and expensive to buy but the temptation to buy a cheap, common bull should be resisted.

The points to look for when selecting breeding stock are illustrated in Fig. 18. When choosing a stock bull good weight for age is essential; the bull should be well fleshed, and possess size and scale. Soundness of legs and feet are of the utmost importance, and a bull must walk well if he is to get round a herd of cows at mating time.

Yearling bulls should be restricted to serving not more than twenty cows in their first season if their growth is not to be impaired. Mature bulls may be expected to make sixty or more services a year. Usually, one bull is allocated to forty cows.

Calving date

In the spring calving herds, the cows should be timed to drop their calves six to eight weeks before the spring flush of grass is expected. By this method the calf will be old enough to take the extra milk produced by the cow when the spring grass arrives. If cows do not calve until late April or May, there will be a risk of over-stocked udders and scouring of calves.

Steaming up

The practice of steaming up, which means feeding supplementary concentrates to the in-calf cow during the last few weeks of pregnancy, has long been established in dairy herds. The advantages of steaming up beef cows is now recognized by many farmers, but the practice is by no means general.

The plan is to feed the cows 1–2 kg of balanced concentrates a day from three to four weeks before calving. The amount may be increased slightly as calving approaches, but should not be taken to more than 2 kg a day, or over-stocked udders may occur. Cows that are in poor body condition will obviously benefit most from this extra feeding.

The chief benefits of steaming up are that the calves are heavier and more vigorous at birth, milk yield is increased, the cows are fitter at calving and the risk of disease is lessened.

Calving

Beef cows in hard condition will normally calve out of doors in a sheltered field without any assistance, but a careful eye should be kept on them so that, if difficulties occur, the cow can be brought into a loose box and receive the necessary attention (see page 100).

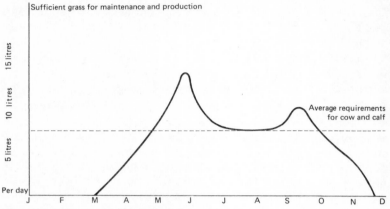

Fig. 25   Estimated seasonal growth of grass

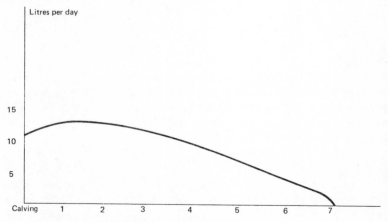

Fig. 26   Estimated lactation curve for beef cow

92

The suckled calf

The well-bred suckling calf has tremendous potential for rapid growth and development of beef characteristics. It is a stockman's job to ensure that the calf is kept healthy, and that it receives the right foods, in order that it may express its full inherited beef characteristics.

Daily routine inspection of the suckling herd is vital. The calves should be seen walking about as well as suckling. The stockman should look at each cow, examining her general health and temperament. If a cow's udder is found to be over-stocked with milk, then it must be milked out immediately, although in some cases it may be possible to suckle the cow with a second calf.

All calves should be ear-tagged as soon as possible with the attested herd number, or ear tattooed if pedigree.

Calf creep

During the suckling period, a calf will receive 1000–1500 litres of milk and grazing; but if the maximum rate of growth is to be achieved, supplementary concentrates must also be fed. A calf creep can easily be made by fencing off a corner of a field. Inside this, and free from interference by the cows, the calves can be fed up to 1–2 kg of calf rearing pencils, or a suitable home mixed ration, a day.

As autumn approaches, good quality hay should also be fed to the calves. This will help to offset the decline in both milk yield and grass.

Given these conditions, the calves may be expected to put on 1 kg live-weight gain per day. This means that the calves should weigh around 200–230 kg at weaning.

In late autumn the calves will grow a dense, thick winter coat. This can easily deceive the farmer into thinking that the calves are still making good growth, when in actual fact they may be losing weight. At this stage the calves should be weaned and brought into the yards.

Castration

Surgical castration is widely adopted in upland herds where there is less risk of wound infection from flies or bacteria. A veterinary surgeon is best employed to castrate the calves if this method is adopted, since considerable skill and the most careful hygiene are needed if the operation is to be successful.

The bloodless Burdizzo method may be carried out at any age up to 3 months. The elastrator and rubber ring method should be done before the calves are a week old.

Disbudding

The removal of the horn buds to prevent the horns growing should be done when the calves are three to four weeks old. Full details for castration and disbudding are given in Chapter 9.

Weaning

At weaning, the calves should be comfortably housed in well-strawed buildings, preferably with an adjoining open yard for exercise.

The sudden change of environment and diet upsets the calves, and there will be some bawling for several days. This stress can be overcome to some extent if the calves are offered green food such as kale or cabbage, which is more appetizing than dry hay and concentrates. Once the calves settle down, they should be fed on a ration aimed at achieving 1 kg a day.

Suckler herds in the lowlands

The arable farm

In recent years, the suckler herd has become very popular on large arable farms. The reason for this is that the beef herd makes the least demand on farm labour; the herd can graze odd, rough grazings, one year leys, and parklands, and if yarded in winter will tread straw to produce large amounts of farmyard manure. The only difference in the management of this type of herd and the upland herd is that the cows calve in the autumn and are frequently large-framed and cross-bred, e.g. Hereford × Friesians. Also, under favourable conditions, it is sometimes possible to double suckle the cows, by purchasing an extra calf.

Autumn calving

Autumn born calves are much stronger and heavier at birth than spring born calves. This is due to the cow having had plenty of grass, exercise and sunshine during the summer. The calves grow steadily through the winter months, especially if they receive creep feed.

In the spring and following summer, the calves will make rapid growth if given good lowland pastures to graze. By autumn, the calves will weigh about 350 kg and will be suitable for fattening as baby beef.

Chapter Eleven
Multiple Suckling

Multiple suckling is a system that allows up to ten calves to be reared successively by a 'nurse' cow, during her lactation. Older dairy cows, past their best for milk production, or those that are slow milkers, or have lost a quarter are suitable for this purpose.

Each calf will need about 400–450 litres of milk during a suckling period of ten to twelve weeks. A cow that yields 3500–4000 litres during her lactation will, therefore, be able to rear eight to ten calves.

Example	*Weeks*	*No. of calves*
	Calving–10	3–4
	11–21	2–3
	22–32	2
	32–42	1

It must be emphasized that the cow will require careful feeding and management during her lactation if she is to provide sufficient milk for eight or more calves.

Suckling

The nurse cow should be tied up by a neck chain for suckling, and the calves brought to her twice a day. Freshly calved cows will suckle up to four calves simultaneously but it is better to suckle two young calves first, then two stronger calves later. This will allow the baby calves to get enough milk, and the stronger pair will empty the udder completely.

As the younger calves grow, they will take more milk and the older calves will gradually be weaned.

Most calves will take to a foster mother immediately, but if difficulty is found it will be necessary for the stockman to assist the calf. This is best done by placing the first finger in the calf's mouth. Once the calf sucks your finger, move its head towards the udder and place the teat in its mouth. Once the calf tastes the milk it will usually suckle.

Occasionally, nurse cows will kick calves away from their udder. If this happens, first check that the udder is not damaged, and then tie a 'kicking strap' in a figure of eight above the hocks on the hind leg.

When the calves have finished suckling, check that the udder is completely empty before releasing the cow. Any sores, cracks, cuts or other damage to the teats must be treated at once with an antiseptic dressing. If hard lumps or hot swelling are found in the udder, veterinary advice should be sought.

Housing

Warm, dry, draught-free pens, which are regularly cleaned and disinfected, will greatly increase the calves' comfort and help to promote rapid growth.

The calves should have access to clean water and good hay at all times. Concentrates should be provided when the calves are one to two weeks old, although if they are receiving plenty of milk they may not eat much before they are about three to four weeks.

Calves reared on this system may be expected to gain 0·5–0·75 kg daily and should, therefore, weigh around 75–100 kg when weaned at 10 weeks. Once weaning is completed the calves' appetite for concentrates will increase rapidly. A rough guide to the amount is to feed 0·5 kg of concentrates per month of age, up to 6 months, and from then onwards to ration the calves at 2·5–3 kg concentrates per day with good hay *ad lib*.

Turning out to grass

Calves born in the autumn and early winter are usually turned out to grass from the middle of April onwards, depending upon weather conditions and the state of the grass. It is advisable to house the stock by night until mid-May in order to reduce the risk of chills and the possible infection by lungworms which can cause 'husk', an infection of the lungs (see page 182).

Spring-born calves should be housed until they reach 150–200 kg live-weight when they may be turned out on to clean, rested, fresh pastures. Leys containing perennial rye-grass and white clover are ideal for growing stock.

Chapter Twelve
Management of Beef Cows

Nurse cows and suckler cows

In upland and hill areas it is customary for heifers to drop their first calves when $2\frac{1}{2}$ or 3 years old. This means that the heifers must be served when either 21 or 27 months old (gestation period 280 days). Thus, spring-born heifers will calve in the autumn $2\frac{1}{2}$ years after birth, or in the following spring, at 3 years.

Compared with the lowland dairy herds, where heifers calve at $2-2\frac{1}{4}$ years, it may seem that beef heifers grow slowly and calve late. However, it should be remembered that, apart from the pre-weaning stage, the heifer is reared on a medium plane of nutrition and subjected to the rigorous climatic conditions found on the hill farm.

Bulling heifers

About every three weeks, though somewhat irregularly during the winter months, the cow or heifer comes on heat. In the summer months, a heifer may be on heat for up to 36 hours, but in the winter months, particularly November and December, a heifer may only be so for a few hours.

During the heat period, the heifer will become excited and will either ride or be ridden on by other cattle. A slight swelling of the vulva may be observed, with a clear, white discharge.

Service

During the act of service, which lasts but a few seconds, the penis of the bull injects about 5 cc of semen into the cow's vagina. Mature bulls are capable of mating sixty cows a year, but young bulls should only be allowed to serve about twenty or so cows in their first season.

Signs of pregnancy

If the heifer does not come on heat again, after being served, it may safely be assumed that she is in-calf (pregnant). About 4 months after mating, one can see a definite enlargement of the abdomen, and from the fifth month of pregnancy one can 'touch' the calf by pressing gently against the right-hand side of the lower flank with one's hand clenched.

From the seventh month onwards you can see the calf 'kick' by watching the lower abdomen; this is often more apparent after the cow has drunk cold water.

During the later stages of pregnancy, the heifer will usually become docile, the abdomen will greatly enlarge and the udder will develop noticeably.

In-calf heifers are generally managed as 'followers'. That is, they follow the main breeding herd at pasture, cleaning up the grazing by eating what the suckler cows and calves have left. During the last six weeks of the gestation, however, the down-calvers should be steamed up with either home-mixed concentrates or a proprietary dairy ration. Single-suckling cows may receive 2 kg concentrates daily, but multiple-suckling cows may safely be fed up to 3 or 4 kg concentrates per day during the last stages of gestation.

Example: Multiple-suckling cow expected to yield 15–20 litres of milk per day when freshly calved

Weeks before calving	kg daily
6–5	1·0–1·5
5–4	1·5–2·0
4–3	2·0–2·5
3–2	2·5–3·0
2–calving	3·0–4·0

Signs of calving

A few days before the heifer is due to calve, her udder will fill with colostrum. The teats will become turgid and the udder may be distended. A waxy substance can be drawn from the teats at this time.

The vulva will enlarge, and at the same time the ligaments around the pelvic girdle will slacken. About 24 hours before calving it will be possible to feel this slackness by placing a hand into the pelvic area.

Calving

Calving is really one continuous process, but for the convenience of description it may be divided into three stages: the dilation stage, the expulsion stage and the cleansing.

The first stage of calving is the dilation of the cervix, in order to allow the calf to pass into the vagina. As the cervix slowly opens, the cow becomes uncomfortable, mild pains make her restless, and she will frequently stand up and then lie down again. The stage ends when the cervix is fully dilated and the cow forces the 'water bags' from the uterus through the vaginal passage.

The water bags consist of sheets of membrane that surround the calf whilst in the uterus. Inside the membrane are fluids which act as a cushion for the developing embryo. At calving, the water bags are first pushed through the cervix and along the vagina; they help to 'open up' the passage, and finally, by rupturing, help to lubricate the walls of the vagina.

The second stage is the expulsion of the foetus, terminating in

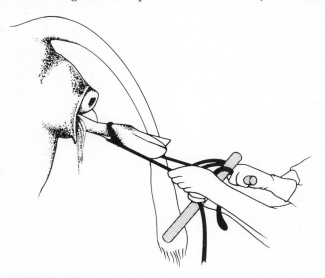

Fig. 27 Gentle assistance with a large calf: pull downwards

the birth of the calf. The labour pains increase and the cow pushes the calf forward. The calf's front legs are first to appear and the head should be resting between the hock joints.

Once the head clears the vulva, the cow will take a short rest, before finally pushing the shoulders through. This is the hardest part of the calving, and gentle assistance may be necessary, with large calves, to get the shoulders away. As the calf clears the passage, it will drop to the ground, breaking the umbilical cord in the process.

Expulsion of the afterbirth, commonly called the cleansing, may take place immediately after the birth or up to 1–2 days later. If a cow retains her cleansing for more than 3 days, consult a veterinary surgeon.

The calf

The cow will almost certainly lick her calf immediately it is born. Licking has a beneficial effect for it aids the calf's respiratory system, removes the slime, and helps to dry the calf.

Should the calf be weakly or reluctant to stand up, the stockman may assist by removing any mucus from the nostrils, then blowing into the calf's mouth until he is satisfied that the calf is breathing normally. It is sound practice to treat the calf's navel with a mild antiseptic to prevent disease entering the body via the wet navel cord.

Malpresentations and difficult calvings

Occasionally it may be necessary to assist the cow at calving, either by applying gentle traction to a large calf or by correcting the position of a calf that is wrongly presented.

If the water bags have appeared and burst and the cow is straining yet there is no sign of the calf's feet appearing, then you should make a preliminary examination. Fetch a bucket of clean, warm water and tablet of soap. Thoroughly wash your hands and arms and work up a soapy lather on your hands which will act as a lubricant. Keeping your hand in a cupped position, gently insert it into the vagina, enter the womb and find the calf. Once you have diagnosed the calf's position you may gently and carefully correct the presentation and calve the cow. However, if you are the least bit undecided then call in the vet immediately for in extreme cases a Caesarian operation may be necessary.

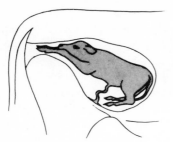 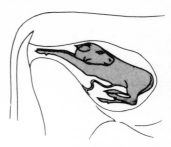

Fig. 28 (a)   Normal presentation   *Fig. 28 (b)*   Head twisted back

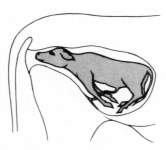 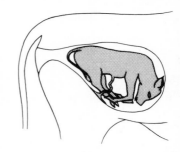

Fig. 28 (c)   Forelegs back   *Fig. 28 (d)*   Breech presentation

In Fig. 28(a) we can see the normal presentation of a calf. If this is the case, all that is needed is a gentle pull on the forelegs to ease the calf through. Pull each leg alternately so that the calf is inched forward.

Once the head appears, pull the calf downwards. At this stage keep the calf moving, as quite often the hip bones catch in the pelvic girdle which makes the calving more strenuous for the cow. A common problem, especially with heifers, is getting the head through the vulva – the forehead is held by the strong muscular tissue which makes up the vulva. Gentle massage with soap and water around this muscular ring will often release the pressure. You may be able to stretch your fingers into the calf's eye sockets and gently pull downwards to overcome this difficulty.

In Fig. 28(b) a calf is shown with its head turned back. To correct this, slide your hand along the neck until you can feel the head and then gently turn it until the nose points forward. If you hold the nose and guide it towards the pelvic opening the cow will push the calf forward when she strains. Once the head and legs are through there should be little difficulty in completing the calving. If you experience some difficulty with the head, then slip a calving rope, tied in a noose, around the back of the head and looped through the mouth.

By running the cord through the mouth and not under the jaw you will avoid strangling the calf.

Fig. 28(c) shows a calf with its forelegs turned back. This is relatively easy to correct providing the head is not too far forward. Push the calf back and turn the legs. Occasionally, a cow is found with the calf's head out. The calf may be dead or the tongue swollen. Great care is needed and veterinary assistance should be sought immediately.

The breech presentation is shown in Fig. 28(d). Your first problem is to make sure that it is a breech and probably your best guide is to find the calf's tail. Then seek the hind legs and turn them to point backwards. Once the legs and hind quarters are exposed outside the cow keep the calf coming or place a hot towel over the calf's rear. This will prevent the calf from gulping uterine fluids into its mouth before it is born. For in a normal birth the sudden change of temperature from the cow's body heat to atmospheric temperature (often a difference of 20°–30°C) makes the calf take a deep breath. This is similar to you taking a sudden cold bath!

There are many other abnormal presentations, which could be described. However, you will find with experience that no two calvings are alike but if you are gentle with the animal, have patience and use common sense, no doubt you will be able to deal with the majority of calvings. Remember: if in doubt call the vet out.

Chapter Thirteen
Pedigree Breeding and Livestock Improvement

The pedigree stock breeder's function is to breed superior type cattle for sale to commercial farmers for improving their herds. The sale of yearling crossing bulls forms the basis of their business, but occasionally a high-priced breeder's bull may be raised.

Bull rearing

Bull calves must be reared on a high plane of nutrition if they are to express their full growth potential and beef qualities.

The selected calves should be housed when they are two to three months old and their dams brought in for suckling twice a day.

In some herds breeders allow valuable bull calves to suckle nurse cows in addition to their dam. From a long-term breeding point of view this is undesirable since it may lead to strains of beef cattle being bred that are incapable of rearing their own calves under field conditions of single suckling.

The calf should be fed rearing pencils, soft meadow hay, and provided with a clean supply of water at all times. After four months a small feed of chopped swedes, mangolds, cow cabbage or soaked sugar beet pulp may be fed as a succulent to stimulate the calf's appetite.

When the calf reaches six months, the hay may be restricted to about 2–3 kg per day and the concentrates increased. If you prefer to feed a home mix rather than purchase rearing pencils, then the following should prove satisfactory:

2 parts rolled oats
2 parts coarse bran
1 part flaked maize
$\frac{1}{2}$ linseed cake
Proprietary minerals and vitamins

A careful eye must be kept on young bulls to detect early signs of loss of appetite or ill health. If an animal goes off its food, then remove what is left in the trough and keep the food away for twelve hours or so. A mild purgative may be given or the animal turned out in a small paddock to graze. 'Never feed an animal more than it will clear up in twenty minutes' is a good rule to follow if healthy appetites are to be maintained.

Handling and exercise

The young bull should be handled frequently and taught to lead on a halter at an early age. Five to six months is none too soon to begin schooling. To teach a calf to lead, first make sure that the halter, or head collar, fits snugly to the head. The leading cord must always be on the animal's near side (left side), holding the lead cord close to the head. As the calf walks forward, move with it, keeping near to its shoulder. A good tip is to get someone to lead a well-schooled animal in front of the calf being broken.

As the bull calf approaches weaning, regular exercise will be necessary. Young bulls of eight to nine months, probably weighing about 350 kg, require at least twenty minutes' exercise per day or walking about one mile. Walking a bull across soft fields, even ploughed land, will strengthen and develop the leg muscles, tone up the circulation and keep the blood pure. Walking once a week on a hard road should keep the hooves in good shape, but if they do become overgrown then trim immediately.

Fig. 29   Bull stocks in use

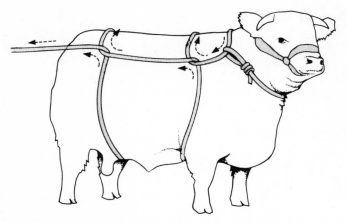

Fig. 30 Casting a beast for foot inspection. Two assistants are necessary: one pulls and holds the rope, while the other holds the halter and restrains the head

Foot trimming

The bull should be either put into bull stocks, a cattle crush, with opening side doors, or cast, in order to trim his feet. Sharp foot-knives, a rasp and a blacksmith's pincers are the tools required for this task. All the trimming should be done from the bottom of the foot. Carefully pare away the soft, overgrown wall until the white line appears. The white line is a clear mark of where the sole of the foot joins the foot wall. The inside of the sole should be trimmed to keep the inside of the foot open.

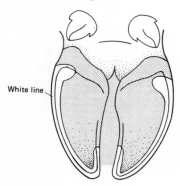

White line

Fig. 31 Foot trimming

Horn training

The horns on the Hereford, Devon and Beef Shorthorn should curve downward and slightly forward. Training is done by weighting the tips with lead weights held in position by leather straps.

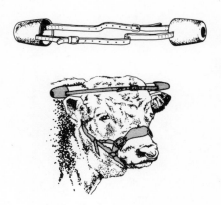

Fig. 32   Horn training and horn weights

The underside of the horn may have a sharp notch filed in, close to the head, to aid the downward movement. Weights should only be used when the horn is firmly fixed to the skull, and should not be kept in place for more than a week at a time. It is advisable to have an interval of two weeks before replacing the weights.

Ringing a bull

It is a bye-law of most auction markets that bulls over one year old should have a ring in the nose before going to auction.

Ringing a bull is quite a simple operation, provided of course that the bull is properly restrained. If a cattle crush is not available a bull may be haltered and put in a pen with a strong half door. An assistant can then hold the halter from outside the pen, with the bull's head over the door. With horned breeds, an additional cord may be placed over the back of the horns.

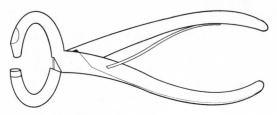

Fig. 33 (a)   Bull nose punch

Fig. 33 (b)   Bull ring with break-off screw

A bull punch is recommended even when using self-piercing bull rings. The usual size ring for a yearling bull is 70 mm and this may later be replaced with a 75 mm ring. The punch is used to cut cleanly through the cartilage. The ring is then placed in position and the holding screw driven home. Any roughness in the metal should be smoothed off with fine emery paper. A little antiseptic ointment may be smeared on the ring to avoid any infection in the nostrils.

Preparation for show or sale

There is nothing that deters attention and interest in a bull more than a dirty, dung-stained coat and tail. All pedigree cattle should be thoroughly cleaned and well-groomed before entering a sale or show yard. Shampooing should be done two or three days before the show so that the hair settles down and becomes more manageable. When the bull is in transit it is preferable to use a halter rather than a head collar so that a proper knot can be put on the halter that will not slip. Two lengths of baling string taken from a bale without cutting is the right length for restraining the tail. Put one length round the neck and make a loop in it; the other length is fastened around the hair at the end of the tail. This length of string is then tied to the loop in the string round the neck. Securing the tail like this prevents the bull soiling his hind quarters and tail whilst in transit.

Washing

On a warm day, thoroughly wash the animal all over, using either a proprietary cattle shampoo or two raw eggs beaten into warm water. Dung soiled parts should be gently soaked until the dirt comes away; avoid using a harsh curry comb which is likely to pull the hairs out at their roots. Rinse the shampoo out of the hair with clean soft water and remove the surplus water with a soft brush or wisp of straw. Keep the animal in a clean, airy, well-strawed loose box.

In winter, lice can ruin the coat very quickly. Regular dusting of the neck, shoulders, tail root, brisket and between the hind legs with a louse powder will avoid this unsightly damage. The sides of the brisket are also important when de-lousing.

Brushing the coat daily will help to stimulate a healthy skin and promote the growth of hair. If practicable the animals may be allowed to run in a small paddock at night, and housed by day. The cold night air will encourage a winter coat to grow.

On the day of the sale, the hooves and horns may be lightly oiled with linseed or olive oil. The head collar, or halter, should be properly cleaned and the stockman should wear a clean, white coat.

Showing

Considerable practice is required by the stockman and the animal if it is to be shown to advantage. A skilled stockman is an artist in this respect. The cattle must be trained to walk with a free movement and to stand well for close inspection by the judge or prospective purchaser. It is best to carry a dandy brush in your pocket to give a final brush to the coat just prior to entering the ring.

Bull performance testing

It is generally accepted by cattle breeders and commercial fatteners that the traits for rapid growth and efficient food utilization are highly heritable factors. Many trials by pedigree breeders, commercial firms, the Milk Marketing Board, Ministry of Agriculture experimental farms, university farms and the Meat and Livestock Commission have all proved this point.

The Meat and Livestock Commission have testing stations where they accept pedigree bull calves for testing when about 200 days old and the young bulls stay on test until 400 days.

The bulls, on arrival, are housed in comfortable surroundings and allowed a few days to settle in. They are then weighed and fed

Fig. 34   Bull testing centre

individually on a standardized ration for the next six months. Strict records are kept of the food consumption and daily live-weight gain. Thus at the end of the test it is possible to calculate the bull's individual performance and to compare this with similar animals kept under identical conditions throughout the testing period.

A panel of breeders assess the bulls for points of conformation, breed character and general soundness of movement and health. At the end of the feeding period each bull is also tested for the amount of backfat covering the eye muscle by the use of an ultra-sonic scan.

Ultrasonic testing

The ultrasonic scan is an electronic machine which indicates the amount of backfat covering the eye muscle (lean meat). This indicates the amount of total bodyfat. Bulls of several breeds have been ultrasonically scanned at the MLC stations to find out if this information can be of use to the bull breeder in selecting future stud bulls.

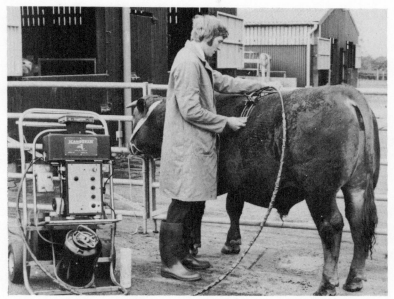

Fig. 35   Ultrasonic scanner in use at a performance test centre

Growth, development and feed use in performance tested bulls (Source: MLC)

During growth, muscle has a higher priority for nutrients than fat. Therefore in a growing beast at low levels of feeding there is little fat development. Yet at the highest levels of feeding, fat accounts for a high proportion of the energy content of carcass gains, even in the young calf. As the beast gets older and heavier an increasing proportion of carcass gains is made up of fat. The general pattern of development is modified by the extent to which there are genetic differences between breeds and between cattle within a breed in the rate of fat deposition. This leads to the concept of early maturity (early fattening) and late maturity (see Chapter 3).

From the cattle feeding viewpoint there are two opposing forces. On the one hand, as daily feed consumption increases so does daily gain. There is a consequent improvement in feed efficiency as a higher proportion of feed intake is used foi growth as opposed to maintenance. On the other hand, as daily gain increases so does the amount of fat in each unit of gain. Because the feed cost of producing 1 kg of fat is seven or eight times greater than producing 1 kg of lean, this effect tends to make feed efficiency worse.

The net result of these opposing forces is that, as feed intake and daily gain increase, feed efficiency continues to improve in spite of the increase in fat deposition because efficiency is influenced more by the amount of feed consumed in excess of maintenance needs than it is by the increased content of fat in the carcass gains. The effect of fatness is seen in the worsening feed efficiency as cattle get older, bigger and fatter.

Within a performance test of bulls fed a high quality diet *ad lib*, it is likely that above-average growth rate and good feed efficiency are associated with above-average fatness. At the other end of the scale very low fatness is associated with low feed intake and its consequences, low growth rate and poor feed efficiency.

Types of bull

From the results collected so far, four basic types of bull have been identified:

(a) Poor all-round performance with a low feed intake, low daily gain and poor feed efficiency. The bull is thin because its performance is low.

(b) Very early maturity with a high feed intake, average daily gain, average feed efficiency and a very high level of fatness.

(c) Large early maturing type with a high feed intake, high daily gain, good feed efficiency and a fairly high level of fatness.

(d) Large late maturing type with a high feed intake, high daily gain, excellent feed efficiency and below average fatness.

The first type of bull is undesirable because of its poor all-round performance and the second type because of excessive fat development at a relatively low live-weight. A choice between the third and fourth types would depend on objectives. The third type would be preferred if selection sought to increase size whilst retaining earliness of maturity. Bulls of the fourth type would be preferred for rapid lean growth. A major factor determining this choice would be the system of production in which the offspring were to be reared. Earliness of maturity is at its greatest advantage in those beef systems relying more on forage because an acceptable level of finish is achieved at slaughter.

Comparative performance of breeds and crosses

Commercial beef units in which different breeds and crosses are reared side by side as contemporaries are an important source of comparative performance information.

Table 6 shows results for dairy-bred steers reared in cereal beef and 18-month beef production. Daily gains and slaughter weights are shown as percentages above or below those for contemporary Friesian steers. The results confirm that the heavier breeds, such as the Charolais and South Devon, sire the fastest growing calves and that slaughter weight is directly related to growth rate. However, the Sussex × Friesian and Hereford × Friesian both grow faster than the Friesian but are earlier maturing and are therefore slaughtered at lighter weights.

Table 6 Comparative performance of breeds and crosses from three months of age to slaughter in cereal beef and 18-month beef production

Breed or cross (steers)	Cereal beef		18-month grass/cereal beef	
	Daily gain	Slaughter weight	Daily gain	Slaughter weight
Charolais × Friesian	+ 8·4	+ 9·1	+10·4	+ 7·2
South Devon × Friesian	+ 7·2	+ 7·8	+ 8·9	+ 4·4
South Devon	+ 6·7	+ 6·1	+ 7·7	+ 2·6
Devon × Friesian	+ 6·7	+ 5·5	+ 6·7	+ 2·4
Lincoln Red	+ 6·4	+ 4·8	+ 7·2	+ 2·8
Sussex × Friesian	+ 3·6	− 2·1	+ 3·4	− 0·9
Hereford × Friesian	+ 3·3	− 5·1	+ 3·1	−10·4
Friesian	0	0	0	0
Angus × Friesian	− 12·1	−14·2	−11·4	−15·7
Ayrshire	− 16·3	− 8·9	−18·9	−13·9

% above (+) or below (−) Friesian steers

Table 7 Comparative performance of breeds and crosses during yard finishing

Breed or cross (steers)	Medium stores (<400 kg)		Heavy stores (>400 kg)	
	Daily gain	Slaughter weight	Daily gain	Slaughter weight
Charolais × Friesian	+ 10·9	+ 6·9	+ 11·3	+ 8·1
South Devon × Friesian	+ 10·7	+ 4·1	+ 10·8	+ 6·2
Lincoln Red × Friesian	+ 6·1	+ 1·4	+ 6·4	+ 1·1
Devon × Friesian	+ 5·8	− 0·5	+ 6·1	+ 1·4
Hereford × Friesian	+ 4·9	− 8·7	+ 1.1	− 10·2
South Devon	+ 4·9	+ 5·1	+ 4·8	+ 5·4
Sussex × Friesian	+ 3·4	− 1·1	+ 3·1	+ 1·3
Devon	+ 2·1	+ 0·8	+ 1·3	+ 1·3
Lincoln Red	+ 1·9	+ 1·1	+ 1·8	+ 1·1
Sussex	+ 0·6	− 0·8	+ 0·4	− 2·5
Friesian	0	0	0	0
Charolais × beef cow	− 5·1	− 7·9	− 6·2	− 8·7
Angus × Friesian	− 13·3	− 10·1	− 16·1	− 12·4
Hereford × beef cow	− 15·8	− 12·9	− 17·2	− 15·0
Angus × beef cow	− 18·6	− 13·3	− 19·9	− 16·2
Beef Shorthorn × beef cow	− 19·3	− 14·1	− 20·7	− 18·0

% above (+) or below (−) Friesian steers

Source: Meat and Livestock Commission.

There is little difference in the order of ranking of breeds and crosses between the two systems of production. Results for the 18-month system combine a grazing season and yard finishing and comparative growth rates are similar in the two periods for all breeds and crosses except the Hereford × Friesian. This last cross had a daily gain 5·7 per cent higher than the Friesian during the grazing season but only 2·8 per cent yard finishing.

Results for the yard finishing of medium and heavyweight stores presented in Table 7 show a generally higher level of growth and greater slaughter weights for crosses out of Friesian cows than for crosses out of suckler cows. Within each cow type the heavier sire breeds again usually produced the highest growth rates and slaughter weights.

Chapter Fourteen
The Common Farm Foods and their Utilization

Feeding-stuffs can be broadly classified into four main groups, namely green fodders, coarse fodders, succulents and concentrates.

Green fodders

Green fodders consist of grasses, clovers, cereals such as grazing oats or rye, herbs, and to some extent, weeds. They are characterized by a high moisture content and a fairly high fibre content, although the fibre is usually more digestible than that of the coarse fodders. They contain the yellow pigment carotene which is the precursor of vitamin A. Their nutritive value depends on the stage of growth at which they are fed. This is discussed later under the heading of grassland utilization.

Coarse fodders

Roughages (or coarse fodders) consist of hay, straw and chaff. They are bulky foods with a high dry matter content – often 80–85 per cent. Fibre content is usually between 30–40 per cent, and much of this is indigestible.

Succulents

The common factor here is a low dry matter, high moisture content. Mangolds, swedes, turnips and potatoes are good examples. Succulent foods are liked by stock and often fed to stimulate the animal's appetite.

Concentrate foods

These foods contain a relatively high proportion of nutrients per unit of weight, hence the term concentrate. They are high in dry matter – usually 80–85 per cent. Their use is generally restricted to production rations for milk or meat. Concentrates are often subdivided into protein concentrates which are foods with a high proportion of protein, i.e. 40 per cent or more protein equivalent (PE); and carbohydrate concentrates which are high in starch equivalent (SE) but low in protein – about 10 per cent protein equivalent.

Grassland utilization

Grass is a crop and must be utilized efficiently. Many farmers are inefficient and wasteful in the way they utilize grass. To get the most out of grass it must be harvested efficiently either by the grazing animal or by various means of conservation. This means cutting the grass for conservation at the correct stage of growth, grazing grass at the correct stage of growth and achieving the correct stocking density.

The diagram below shows the optimum stages of growth for the best utilization of grass under grazing, silage and hay management systems. This shows the height and digestibility of the grass at each growth stage in terms of utilization.

Digestibility is measured in terms of *D value*. The D value is the *percentage of digestible organic matter in the total dry matter*, e.g. 60D indicates that there is 60 kg of digestible energy producing organic matter in 100 kg of dry feed.

Too early to utilize

When very young grass is actively tillering and growing, grazing at this stage weakens young plants and reduces tillering. The amount of grass available for grazing is also considerably less than when grass is grazed at the 125–200 mm stage. Grass is often grazed at this stage in early spring by sheep, which results in slow recovery and poor late spring grazing when grass is required by cows.

Ideal stage for grazing

This is at the 125–200 mm stage (before ear emergence) for dairy cattle and beef cattle and at the 80–100 mm stage for sheep. The leaves at this stage have broadened and there are many of them as

116

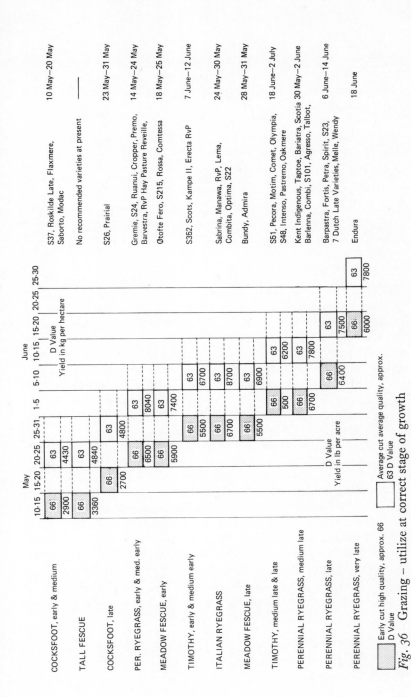

Fig. 36 Grazing – utilize at correct stage of growth

tillering has taken place. The D value of grass at this stage is 70–75 and the protein content is high.

The feeding value is very high when grass is grazed at this stage and grass will give up to:

> Maintenance plus 20–25 litres per day
> (dependent on calving date)

or

> Maintenance plus 0·9 kg per day with little or no concentrates.

The feeding value of grass when grazed at this stage will produce more output per hectare than grass at any other stage of growth. It is also more palatable so the animal will eat more of it, thus raising production still higher. Normally an interval of 21–28 days between grazings will produce grass of this quality.

Conservation

When conserving grass the main objective is to cut at the optimum stage of growth which will give the most acceptable compromise between quantity and quality. For an average cut of average quality, the National Institute of Agricultural Botany (NIAB) have set a figure of 63D; for early cut, high quality but lower quantity; a corresponding figure has been set at 66D value. Losses in terms of digestibility occur during the conservation process; these depend on mechanical treatment, effects of weather, type of fermentation, additives, method of drying, etc. These losses can vary from 2–10 digestibility units and are lowest in dried grass and barn dried hay and highest in silage and field cured hay. The date at which the crop reaches the 63D value can be delayed by (a) presence of white clover, which maintains a D value of over 70 for a long period of time and (b) spring grazing which can delay heading by up to one week but reduces yield of grass. For subsequent cuts an average level of 63D is reached after seven weeks' regrowth except in the case of Italian ryegrass and cocksfoot when it falls to this level after five weeks' regrowth. The dates at which the various grass species are at 66D and 63D values are shown in Fig. 36. These should be borne in mind when compiling a seeds mixture suitable for hay or silage.

Silage stage

This is just before or on commencement of the emergence of the seed head. It is important to conserve silage at precisely this stage. Too early a cut results in lower yields and higher moisture contents. Too late a cut (after heading) produces poor fermentation because of the higher fibre content. Cut when the D value is 63–66.

Hay stage

Cut not more than one week after seed head emergence. This results in greater bulk than with silage; the increase in bulk is due mainly to increase in fibre. D values can range from 58–65. This is the stage when the maximum bulk of high digestibility grass can be conserved. A delay of 4–5 days in cutting results in rapid fall in protein percentage and increase in fibre content.

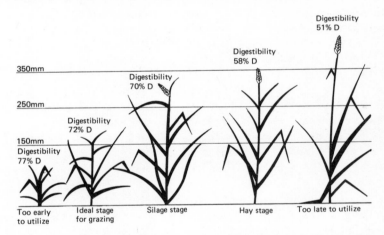

Fig. 37 Average date of cut and DM yields for NIAB recommended grass varieties

Too late to utilize

At this stage there is a lot of bulk but feeding value may be little better than barley straw. Carbohydrates are rapidly being converted into fibre and protein content is low. The future performance of the ley will suffer. The population of shade susceptible grasses, e.g. Meadow Fescue, and clovers will be reduced and young tillers will be smothered. Slow to recover may mean that it takes over two months to produce a grazeable aftermath.

Coarse fodders

Hay

The feeding value of hay varies considerably due to numerous factors; the most important of these are the composition of the sward, the age at cutting and the subsequent weather conditions; and the method of making the hay.

As a generalization one may say that the best hay is made from the leafier species of grass, which are cut just as the ear emerges, and then cured into hay as quickly as possible.

You will be able to recognize good hay by first examining an opened bale and looking for a leafy sweet-smelling green-coloured product. Crops that are 'overmade' will have a straw-like texture and light colour. Crops that have been subjected to heavy rain will be dark, almost black in colour and probably have a 'musty' smell. Dusty hay or moulds are further objections which should be avoided if possible.

Hay may be cut from meadows consisting of 'permanent' grasses, or from young leys of only a few years' duration. The former is known as meadow hay and the latter as seeds hay. Meadow hay is much softer and sweeter-smelling than seeds hay due to the finer species of grasses found in old pasture, such as sweet vernal and the fine meadow grasses. Seeds hay, although somewhat coarser, will generally have a higher feeding value than meadow hay, providing it is well-made.

The first quality hay should always be reserved for the higher-milking cows, calves and growing stock. Poorer hay may be fed to older stock and dry cows. Some of the poorer hay may only have a feeding value similar to barley and oat straw; this is best fed to outlying bullocks.

Hay usually has a binding effect on the bowels, but occasionally for some inexplicable reason may result in a laxative effect. New season's hay is liable to cause digestive upsets if fed in large quantities before Christmas.

Leguminous hay, i.e. made from crops such as lucerne, sainfoin or the clovers, are rich in proteins, calcium and phosphorus but they tend to be somewhat coarse.

The following table shows the wide variation in the feeding values of hay:

	DM	SE	PE
Good red clover hay	85	38	7·0
Lucerne – cut before flowering	85	32	10·0
Good seeds hay	85	40	7·0
Good meadow hay	85	37	4·5
Poor meadow hay	85	28	3·0
Weathered hay	85	20–25	2·0–3·0

Straws and chaff

Straws consist of the stems and leaves of plants after the removal of the ripe seeds by threshing. Chaff consists of the 'husk' or glumes of the seed which are separated from the grain. Both chaff and straw are extremely fibrous, high in lignin and, therefore, low in nutritive value.

The subsequent feed value of straw depends mainly on the ripening of the grain. If corn is under-ripe when harvested, e.g. 'green oats', then the straw will have a higher feed value than if the crop is over-ripe.

Oat straw

Oat straw is generally regarded as the best of the cereal straws for feeding to cattle. In certain areas it is cut whilst the straw is still green and the grain is left unthreshed. Either a binder is used and the crop harvested in sheaves, or the crop is mown and later baled. Under these conditions the feed value will be similar to good quality hay.

However, the majority of oats are combine harvested and this leads to a more brittle straw with a high lignin content. The digestibility of such material may be less than 50 per cent and the starch equivalent only 10–20 per cent.

A further problem with feeding straws is the low voluntary intake by cattle. This can be partly overcome by feeding urea either in liquid form or as a feed block (see page 131). Urea has the effect of stimulating the bacteria in the rumen to break down the plant cellulose. The final effect is to increase the straw's digestibility whilst the voluntary intake is increased by as much as 40 per cent.

Barley straw

Although somewhat different in appearance, barley straw is very similar to oat straw in feeding value. Like oat straw, its nutritive content will vary according to the stage of cutting and harvesting. Spring barleys are generally preferred to winter barley because the straw is less mature and has a lower fibre content. However, it must be remembered that harvesting conditions are usually more favourable for the winter corn and an outbreak of wet weather during mid to late September can seriously affect the feed value of a late sown crop of spring barley.

One other disadvantage of barley straw is the presence of barley awns in the straw. These needle-like structures which are threshed from the grain in harvesting may enter the animal's eyes and lodge under the eyelid, thus causing the animal distress. To avoid this problem it is best to feed the straw on the floor, preferably using a feed barrier rather than using a raised hay rack. Thus the animal will pick the straw up rather than pull it down with the risk of barley awns entering the eyes.

Wheat and rye

These straws are rarely fed to cattle. They are extremely low in feed value and are usually kept for bedding.

Silage

Silage is the product made by controlled fermentation of high moisture crops such as grass, green oats, beans, peas, vetches or maize. By far the most silage is made from grass, although in the more favourable climatic areas, large amounts of maize silage are made.

Well-made silage is extremely palatable and has a slightly laxative effect. As with hay the final quality of the material depends upon the original foods used; their stage of growth, and the way they are ensiled. You cannot expect to put poor quality herbage into a silo and get good quality silage out.

Well-preserved silage can be recognized by its colour, acidity, smell and moisture content. A good sample will have leafy material, be light green with a pleasant aromatic smell and will turn litmus paper red. If subjected to chemical tests the pH will be around 4. Good silage will have a high dry matter content of around 25–30 per cent or higher.

Poor quality silage will have an objectionable colour due to the presence of butyric acid. It may be yellowish or dark brown, due to poor fermentation or 'overheating'. Seepage from rain water into a silo will also affect quality.

Many of the former problems associated with silage making are now overcome by the use of chemical additives used whilst making the silage. Powders or liquids containing weak acids are mixed thoroughly with the crop as it passes through the forage harvester. Chemically treated silage is known as 'cold silage' because the bacterial process is eliminated.

Feeding grass silage

Silage can be fed in two ways: either the cattle are brought to the silage face and allowed to help themselves, i.e. self-feed silage, or the silage is cut and carted to the feed troughs in the cattle yard.

Self-feed silage is the better system for suckler cows and store cattle, the obvious advantage being the saving in manual labour. It has certain drawbacks in that the animals' intake cannot be so closely controlled as when the silage is cut and fed in troughs. The 'boss' cow will overeat and the 'shy' cattle may be underfed. Store cattle, especially those around 18–20 months who are changing their incisor teeth, may have difficulty in pulling sufficient silage from the clamp, especially if the silage is made with long material and heavily consolidated.

This problem can be overcome by cutting the silage and throwing it into a trough in front of the silage face, but, of course, the main advantage of self-feed will be lost.

On fattening farms the silage is generally cut and hauled mechanically. This can mean an automatic unloading device in a tower silo or a tractor and fore-end loader fitted with a grab fork if a traditional silage clamp is used.

Adult and fattening stock will consume upwards of 50 kg of silage per day and if the silage is good quality this will produce maintenance and production of 10–15 litres of milk from the cows, or maintenance and about 0·75 kg live-weight gain in fattening stock. The silage will usually provide all the protein requirements and only a little extra rolled barley and minerals will be needed to get maximum production.

Maize silage

Silage made from forage maize will be slightly higher in starch, but considerably lower in protein than grass silage.
Typical analysis would be:

	DM	SE	D.C.P.	D Value
Maize silage	25	12·2	1·4	68–70
Good grass silage	25	12·0	2·2	60–63

Maize silage can be fed *ad lib* to adult beef cattle, but for best results extra protein and minerals should be added to the ration. This can be done by using a maize silage protein mineral additive when harvesting the crop, or by mixing a protein vitamin supplement with concentrates and feeding with the daily feed of silage, or using a urea liquid feed.

Young cattle will respond to extra concentrates and growth rates of around 1 kg per day can be achieved.

Table 8 Recommended crude protein contents of maize silage diets for cattle of different ages and weights

Age (months)	Weight (kg)	Crude protein % of dry matter
3–6	100–190	16·5
6–9	190–280	15·0
9–15	280–460	12·0

Adapted from MLC, *Maize Silage Beef*.

Table 9   Response of Friesian steers of different ages to increasing the protein of a maize silage diet

	Daily live-weight gain (kg per head) at age (months)		
Diet	3–6	6–9	9–12
Maize silage *ad lib*, no supplement	0·45	0·59	0·95
Maize silage *ad lib*, plus 1½% urea in daily dry matter intake	0·59	1·0	1·0
Maize silage *ad lib*, plus 1½% urea and 20% dried lucerne in daily dry matter intake	0·9	1·09	1·0

Adapted from MLC, *Maize Silage Beef.*

Succulents

Cabbage and kale

Cow cabbage and kale provide an appetizing winter feed for suckling cows and young stock. They are invaluable in autumn calving beef herds, providing high protein food to supplement the declining growth of grass and supplementary dry food.

Kales are available in three forms, namely Marrow Stem, Thousand Head and hybrid varieties.

Marrow Stem is a variety which has a thickened fleshy stem; it is high-yielding and will provide forage up to Christmas and into the New Year if weather conditions are favourable. Thousand Head kale derives its name from the mass of budded foliage it carries. It is more frost resistant than Marrow Stem. For this reason it is usually reserved for feeding after Christmas. There are several strains of Thousand Head kale ranging from dwarf types such as Canson which stands 60 cm high to Hungry Gap which grows to about 1 m high.

The hybrid varieties are basically similar to Marrow Stem but are considerably hardier and provide a higher yield of digestible material.

Cabbage and kale is usually fed *in situ* by strip grazing with an electric fence. Adult stock will eat about 20–25 kg if allowed approximately two hours' grazing or about 5–6 m² of an average crop when strip grazing.

Sugar beet tops

These are the crowns and leaves of sugar beet which are removed from the roots at harvest time. They are a highly digestible crop and have a feeding value similar to kale.

Care should be taken in feeding to ensure that the tops are reasonably clean and wilted for about two weeks. The effect of wilting is to reduce the level of oxalic acid in the leaf. Feeding chalk with the tops will help to prevent the risk of oxalic poisoning.

Adult stock may be fed upwards of 30 kg of tops per day. The tops may be either carted to the stock or fed in the field behind an electric fence.

Swedes

Swedes are the most popular of the root crops grown for stockfeed. They have a higher feeding value than mangolds and have the added advantage of being suitable for mechanical harvesting and handling. They provide excellent feed for all types of beef cattle: calves especially do well on a ration which includes sliced swedes, whilst stronger cattle may receive the roots whole.

On fattening farms the swedes may be fed *ad lib* from a self-feeding hopper. A 500 kg steer would consume about 30 kg of swedes per day in addition to its ration of good quality hay.

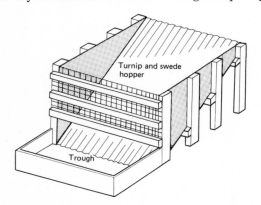

Fig. 38   Fixed self-feed turnip and swede hopper

Mangolds

This crop was once widely grown on livestock farms because it produced the highest tonnage of dry matter per hectare of any farm crop. Unfortunately, the high cost of growing and the enormous amount of hand labour involved in singling and harvesting makes the crop uneconomic today.

Mangolds are ideal for supplementing second quality hay or good feeding straw when fed to store cattle in winter as their succulence makes the feed more appetizing and balances the costiveness of dry food. Mangolds may be fed whole to mature cattle, but should be sliced when fed to calves.

Freshly lifted mangolds contain a high content of amides and these are likely to cause digestive upsets if the roots are fed too soon. It is best, therefore, not to feed the crop until after Christmas when the roots have matured.

Concentrate foods: carbohydrate-rich

Barley

This is the most important cereal crop grown for cattle feed. It may be fed either 'rolled' or ground into meal. Some merchants cook barley and then run it through heavy rollers to produce barley flakes. Barley may be fed in large amounts (see page 153 for barley beef) to fattening stock, or included in growing rations at around 50–60 per cent of the ration.

Barley is less fibrous than oats, has a low oil content and is rich in starch. It should be remembered, however, that samples of grain vary considerably in quality and, therefore, feeding value. The farmer should always look for a plump grain with a thin skin and golden colour. By cutting the grain it is possible to observe the starch content – a full, white grain indicates a good sample. Always avoid shrivelled, thick-skinned grain with a weathered appearance for its feeding value will be considerably lower than quality grain.

Oats

Rolled oats are an excellent feed for all cattle and in particular young growing calves. It has a higher fibre content than barley and is lower in energy. In recent years barley feeding has largely replaced oats but this is mainly due to the economics of growing the crop and not the feeding value. With the introduction of higher yielding varieties the oat crop could possibly regain some of its former popularity.

Stockmen who feed large quantities of grain to cattle, e.g. rearing bulls, often prefer to feed oats rather than barley because they consider it to be a safe food, with less risk of digestive upsets, due to the higher fibre content of oats. The higher oil content also helps to give the cattle a good bloom on their coats.

Although the majority of farmers feed oats rolled or crushed, some feeders include whole oats in the ration.

Flaked maize

Flaked maize is produced by cooking whole maize and then passing it through rollers. The process produces extremely palatable and highly nutritious flakes. This makes flaked maize a valuable food for young stock and sick animals where palatability is important.

Flaked maize is also useful as a 'tracer' food when mixing two rations on the farm. The calf rearing ration will thus have 'yellow flakes' and the cattle fattening ration will be identified by the absence of flakes.

Sugar beet pulp

This is the residue left after sugar has been extracted from the sugar beet. The pulp is usually dried at the factory and sold in cubes or in its natural form. Wet sugar beet pulp is available to farmers who reside near to the factory and are able to collect the material regularly. Obviously the cost of transport and the short keeping life of wet pulp restricts the widespread use of the food.

However, on the farm the dried beet pulp may be soaked in water and fed as a succulent or included dry in a balanced ration. Adult stock should not receive more than 2 kg of dried beet pulp per day due to the risk of it swelling inside the animal.

Coarse bran

Bran is a by-product of the milling industry. It is relatively low in feeding value but has excellent physical properties. It may, for example, be fed in the form of a warm Bran Mash to sick animals whereby it will have a mild laxative effect. A Bran Mash is made by placing 1–2 kg of bran in a bucket and pouring hot water over the top – leave to cool and then feed. Bran may also be fed dry to animals that are scouring (acute diarrhoea) in this case it will have a binding effect.

In general, bran is not included in the normal rations because of its bulk and high cost in relation to feed value, but rather kept for special rations such as those fed to stock raised for show purposes, young bulls, sick animals and calves.

Concentrate foods: protein-rich

Groundnut cakes and meals

This food is available either as decorticated or undecorticated. Decorticated groundnut is the residue from imported groundnuts after the oil and outer husk is removed – the undecorticated form is of lower feeding value due to the outer husk being left in the food. Decorticated groundnut may be purchased in cake, meal or pellets and is the most widely used protein food for calves and growing stock. It is very palatable and liked by stock. The undecorticated cake is less palatable and usually fed to adult stock only.

Cotton cake

Like groundnut this food is available as decorticated or undecorticated cake or meal. It is not as palatable as groundnut and so is usually fed to adult animals rather than calves.

Undecorticated cotton cake contains the seed hulls and also varying amounts of cotton fibre and is greenish brown in colour, whereas the decorticated form is yellow.

Because of its costive effect on the animals' bowels, cotton cake is sometimes fed to fattening stock receiving large amounts of roots or sugar beet tops.

Linseed cake

This is a very popular food for calves and fattening cattle, because apart from its palatability and nutritive value it imparts a bloom to the animals' coats.

Linseed cake tends to be expensive in terms of unit cost but is still widely used. Breeders of pedigree animals who regularly show their cattle will always include linseed cake in rations to maintain their cattle in excellent condition.

Peas and beans

These two foods have the advantage of being home grown, and supply a valuable protein food. A mixture of equal parts of beans and oats will provide a balanced ration for milk production.

Beans should be fully mature before feeding. Freshly harvested beans tend to be soft and are difficult to grind, often leading to a pasty meal which can cause problems with digestion.

Urea (non-protein nitrogen)

Urea is a non-protein food which contains nitrogen (NPN). The nitrogen is broken down into ammonia by bacteria which live in the rumen and subsequently rebuilt into their body protein. Thus cattle and sheep (ruminants) can manufacture their own protein requirements when fed urea either in liquid or solid form.

Urea is produced commercially by synthetic processes and is a white crystalline organic compound in its pure state. Manufacturers blend the urea with molasses, trace elements, vitamins and other additives to produce a safe, palatable and economic feed.

A further advantage is that when the rumen receives regular small doses of urea, the bacteria population increase rapidly and not only produce more protein, but break down a larger proportion of the fibre found in low cost foods such as second quality hay and feeding straws. Thus more nutrients are released from such foods.

Liquid feeding

Liquid feed is offered in self-feeders, using a ball lick. As the animal licks the ball it rotates and picks up further amounts of urea in the treacle carrier.

Thus the animal supplies its rumen with regular small doses of NPN for the celluloytic bacteria to feed on. This in turn results in the animal developing a self-rationing system. For if it receives low quality roughage it will need more bacteria to break down the cellulose and will take in more urea. If, on the other hand, the beast is fed a high energy diet then its consumption of urea will fall.

Liquid feed may safely be offered to calves when around 5–6 months old. It should always be introduced gradually and an introductory period of 3–4 weeks allowed before the full benefits can be expected. Store cattle fed on low energy roughages may, however, be introduced to NPN more abruptly.

A typical ration for an intensive barley beef system would be:

Hay 1 kg
Rolled barley *ad lib*
Liquid feed 0·5 litre

A ration for semi-intensive beef of approximately 400–450 kg:

Hay 5kg
Roots 10 kg
Rolled barley 2 kg
Liquid feed 0·75 litre

Feeding blocks

There are several different types of feeding blocks available from manufacturers. Although basically similar in that they all provide NPN they differ in the proportions of ingredients, binding agents, additives, size and weight. Some include additives such as rumen stimulants and anthelmintics.

The carrier of urea in blocks is usually barley or maize instead of molasses as in liquid feeds. This means that the cereal carrier will also contribute a small percentage of vegetable protein in addition to the added NPN.

Feeding blocks are designed to provide the animal with urea on a 'little and often' basis, that is, the animal licks the block rather than biting or eating. Intake varies according to the size of animal and the quality of food fed but, generally, is around 0·5–0·75 kg for adult stock.

The main advantage of block feeding for the farmer is in hill and upland areas where blocks can easily be taken out to the field and used to assist winter grazing and supplement roughages. On lowland farms they are useful for store cattle and rearing heifers being outwintered.

Dry feed urea

Urea is also supplied in dry form for inclusion in cereal rations providing part of the protein requirements.

Some of these manufactured supplements contain only urea, while others use a mixture of conventional protein together with cereals, minerals, vitamins and trace elements.

Buying raw materials

When purchasing foods such as hay, feeding straw or concentrates, it is worth while to calculate the cost per unit of starch equivalent per tonne.

For example, if good hay costs £40 per tonne and barley straw £15 per tonne which is less expensive?

$$\text{Good hay} = \frac{£40}{36 \text{ SE}} = £1 \cdot 11 \text{ per unit}$$

$$\text{Barley straw} = \frac{£15}{18 \text{ SE}} = 83\text{p per unit}$$

Similarly, if oats cost £50 per tonne, barley £60 per tonne and flaked maize £70 per tonne which is the best buy?

$$\text{Oats} = \frac{£50}{64 \text{ SE}} = 78\text{p per unit}$$

$$\text{Barley} = \frac{£60}{71 \text{ SE}} = 89\text{p per unit}$$

$$\text{Flaked maize} = \frac{£70}{84 \text{ SE}} = 83\text{p per unit}$$

Table 10   Common farm foods: Summary and analysis

	DM	SE	PE
Roughages			
Hay: Quality variable according to botanical composition of sward, stage of growth when cut and haymaking conditions			
Good hay	85	36	4–5
Medium	85	20–30	2–4
Barley straw: Most common feed straw	86	20–23	0·7
Oat straw: Excellent feed if cut when under-ripe	86	20–22	0·9
Oats in sheath: Unthreshed crop – similar in feed value to good hay			
Wheat straw: Used for bedding – very little feed value	86	13	0·1
Green fodders			
Grass: Very variable – feed value depends on grass species, stage of growth and time of year when grazed	20–25	11–15	1·5–2·0
Kale: Excellent winter feed for suckling cows and stores. High in protein. Feed value drops considerably after severe frosts	15	10	1·4
Sugar beet tops: Similar in feed value to kale, allow access to ground chalk to prevent digestive troubles. Wilt tops before feeding	16	8·6	1–1
Root crops: Succulents high in moisture			
Mangolds: Produces high yield per hectare. Little grown today due to high cost of production. Feed after Christmas following a period of storage	12	6	0·4
Swedes: Popular root crop – higher feed value than mangolds and suitable for mechanical harvesting and feeding	12	7·3	0·7
Stubble turnips: Widely grown 'catch crop' following corn – fed *in situ* using			

	DM	SE	PE
electric fence. Feed value varies according to ratio of leaf to root	12	4·5	0·4
Potatoes: Stockfeed potatoes available in years of over-supply. 2 kg potatoes will replace 1 kg hay. Slight risk of choking	23	18	0·8

Concentrates: Carbohydrate-rich

	DM	SE	PE
Oats: Safe food to feed due to high fibre content. Best rolled	87	60	8
Barley: Most widely used cereal due mainly to higher yields than oats and higher energy. Should be rolled or ground	87	71	7·3
Maize meal: High in energy, but should be restricted to not more than 15 per cent of ration for fattening stock due to risk of producing soft, yellow fat	87	78	7·6
Flaked maize: Extremely palatable, liked by stock. Excellent for calves and 'show' cattle	87	89	10
Dried sugar beet pulp: Available also in cubes and blocks. May be fed dry in limited quantity or soaked in water and fed as a succulent	90	60	5
Bran: By-product of milling industry. Has a laxative effect if fed wet and binding if fed dry	87	42	10
Dried grass: Variable in quality and supply	90	40–50	8–10
Palm kernel meal: Gritty texture, somewhat unpalatable	89	73	17

Concentrates: Protein-rich

	DM	SE	PE
Decorticated groundnut cake: Widely used food, palatable and high in protein	90	73	41
Soya bean meal: Pale yellow in colour, rather gritty. High quality protein but usually more expensive than groundnut	86	69	37

	DM	SE	PE
White fish meal: Extremely high value protein of animal origin. Sometimes included in calf rations but too expensive for adult cattle	87	59	53
Linseed cake: Reddish-brown colour, palatable. Gives a bloom to coat. Usually fed to calves and 'show' cattle only	89	74	25
Peas and beans: Homegrown protein food, produces a white, firm fat when included in fattening rations	86	66–69	18–20

Non-protein nitrogen foods

Urea: Supplied in a carefully blended mixture of urea, vitamins, minerals and additives either mixed in a 'carrier' of molasses for liquid feed or in a cereal mixture for feed blocks.
Liquid feed
Feed blocks

Analysis of foods taken from HMSO Bulletin 48, *Rations for Livestock.*

References

Non-protein Nitrogen for Cattle and Sheep, A. J. Rowlinson, Feed Service (Livestock) Ltd., 1973.
The Role of Minerals in Ruminant Nutrition, R. G. Hemingway, Feed Service (Livestock) Ltd., 1973.
The Commercial Development of Urea Based Feeding Systems, A. J. Rowlinson, Feed Service (Livestock) Ltd., 1973.

Chapter Fifteen
Rations for Beef Cattle

The nurse cow

Cows kept for multiple suckling should be managed and fed in almost the same way as commercial dairy cows. The cow that suckles three or four calves will probably yield 15–20 litres of milk per day and will need to be fed accordingly. Single suckling cows, on the other hand, will only produce around 5–8 litres per day and their requirements, therefore, will be considerably less.

When formulating rations for suckling cows, it is convenient to divide the food requirements into two parts, namely maintenance and production.

Maintenance ration

This is the amount of food the mature cow requires to maintain body condition and health. Maintenance requirements vary according to breed, weight, age, condition of cow, and management. The latter point is most important, for cows that are outwintered on an exposed hill farm will require considerably more food than a cow housed in warm, dry surroundings.

There is also considerable variation amongst breeds, for example the Jersey house cow may well consume more energy per 100 kg live-weight than a large-framed Friesian cow suckling calves.

The following table should be used as a guide only, bearing in mind the points just raised.

Table 11

	Maintenance energy requirements (kg. SE per day)	Maintenance protein requirements (kg SP per day)
Jersey	2·5	0·25
Ayrshire	2·8	0·28
Shorthorn	2·9	0·29
Hereford	3·0	0·30
Friesian	3·3	0·33
Charolais South Devon }	3·5	0·35

Production ration

This refers to the food utilized by the cow to produce milk, increase in live-weight, and to feed the developing embryo, if pregnant. If cows are fed in excess of their maintenance and production requirements, then the surplus energy is usually converted into fat. If cows are underfed their performance will drop, although freshly calved cows often utilize stored body condition to produce milk. Hence the saying 'cows milking off their backs'.

Table 12 gives the production requirements for milk per litre, depending on its butterfat content. Beef breeds and their crosses produce milk higher in fat than pure-bred Friesians, but slightly less than Jerseys or Guernseys.

Table 12 Starch and protein requirements for producing milk of varying quality

% Butterfat	(per litre)	
	Kg starch	Kg protein
3·5–3·9	0·25	0·05
4·0–4·4	0·27	0·05
4·5–4·9	0·30	0·06
5·0–5·3	0·32	0·06

Appetite

The cow's appetite governs the amount of food she is able to eat each day. The standard measurement here is the Dry Matter

Content. There is an approximate relationship between the live-weight of the animal and the dry matter content of the food. For milking cows this varies between 2·5 and 2·7 kg per 100 kg live-weight. Beef breeds tend to consume less than the pure dairy breeds. Thus a beef cow weighing around 500 kg will consume approximately $5 \times 2·5 = 12·5$ kg of dry matter per day. A pure-bred dairy cow would require $5 \times 2·7 = 13·5$ kg of dry matter per day. These amounts must, of course, contain all the starch, protein, vitamins and minerals necessary for maintenance and production.

In practice, it will be found that individuals vary; some cows have bigger appetites than others of the same weight, and the foods fed will affect the speed of digestion. On a highly laxative diet like kale, the cow feels hungry sooner than if fed a more costive diet such as oat straw.

Foods used

Homegrown foods, such as hay, silage, sugar beet tops, kale, mangolds, oat and barley straw are used for maintenance rations and sometimes produce the first 5 litres of milk. Where a cow produces more than 5 litres of milk per day, then supplementary concentrate foods like cereals are used.

Compiling rations

Let us take as an example a single suckling Hereford cow producing approximately 5 litres of milk per day. The cow's theoretical feed requirements (see tables 11 and 12) would be:

Single suckling Hereford cow	SE (kg)	PE (kg)
Maintenance	3·0	0·3
Production 5 litres	1·25	0·25
$(5 \times 0·25$ and $5 \times 0·05)$		
	4·25	0·55

If we feed medium quality hay (see table on page 133) with 30 SE, 4·0 PE, 85 DM, the calculations will be:

$$\text{Starch requirements} = \frac{100}{30 \text{ SE}} \times \frac{4·25 \text{ kg}}{1} = \text{approx. 14 kg hay}$$

138

$$\text{Protein requirements} = \frac{100}{4 \cdot 0 \text{ PE}} \times \frac{0 \cdot 55}{1} = \text{approx. 14 kg hay}$$

Our final check must be to see if the dry matter is sufficient to satisfy the appetite and provide the essential nutrients, thus:

$$\frac{14 \text{ kg hay}}{100} \times \frac{85 \text{ DM}}{1} = \text{approx. 13 kg DM}$$

This would be about right for a 500 kg cow but, if she appeared to be hungry, then feed an extra kilogram of barley straw.

We will now consider the requirements for a big South Devon cow suckling four calves and probably producing around 20 litres of milk per day. We shall need to feed better quality hay than for the single suckling cow and supplement this with balanced concentrates. Thus:

South Devon cow	SE (kg)	PE (kg)
Maintenance	3·5	0·33
Production 20 litres	5·0	1·00
(20 × 0·25 and 20 × 0·05)		
	8·3	1·33

Starch requirements using hay with 35 SE, 4 PE, 85 DM:

$$\text{Maintenance} = \frac{35}{100} \times \frac{3 \cdot 5}{1} = 10 \text{ kg hay}$$

and dairy cake with 72 SE, 14 PE, 85 DM:

$$\text{Production} = \frac{100}{72} \times \frac{5}{1} = 7 \text{ kg cake}$$

The dry matter fed will be:

$$\text{Hay:} \quad \frac{85}{100} \times \frac{10}{1} = 8 \cdot 5 \text{ kg}$$

$$\text{Cake:} \quad \frac{85}{100} \times \frac{7}{1} = 5 \cdot 95 \text{ kg}$$

$$\text{Total} = 14 \cdot 45 \text{ kg}$$

This would be quite satisfactory. The protein requirements are calculated in a similar way. It should be noted, however, that the ratio of protein equivalent to starch equivalent in maintenance rations is 1:10 (see table on page 137) whilst for production rations this narrows to 1:4·5–5·0 depending on milk quality (see table 12).

The worked examples are both theoretically correct, but it must be emphasized that cows are individuals. What will do for one beast may not suit another. It is a stockman's job to study his cows, and manage them accordingly. It must also be admitted that working out rations on a SE and PE basis is a time consuming operation and one which is not favoured by most farmers! A simplified method is the *hay equivalents system*. Although not as theoretically accurate, this method is a useful practical guide.

Hay equivalents The basis of the hay equivalent is to compare various feeding stuffs with good quality hay. Since the SE of good hay is 36, if we commit the table of hay equivalents to memory, we can easily remember the SE of most foods.

Table 13   Hay equivalents

	To replace 1 kg hay (36 SE)	
Foodstuff	kg	SE
Barley meal	0·5	71
Oats in sheaf	1·0	36
Oat straw	2·0	18
Wet grains	2·0	18
Potatoes	2·0	18
Grass silage	3·0	12
Kale	4·0	9
Cabbage	4·0	9
Sugar beet tops	4·0	9
Swede	5·0	7·3
Mangold	6·0	6·0
Turnips	8·0	4·4

In practice we do not restrict maintenance rations to hay, but include kale, silage, mangolds, etc. If we wish to replace say 5 kg of hay with silage, we simply refer to Table 13. Silage has a hay equivalent of 3, and therefore 5 kg hay may be replaced by 5 × 3 = 15 kg silage.

Hay equivalent rations In theory a cow requires a little under 1 kg of good hay per 50 kg live-weight. In practice we allow 1 kg per 50 kg l.w., or 10 kg per 500 kg beast, as this will allow for a slight wastage in feeding. We may also allow 3–3·5 kg of good hay to produce 5 litres of milk or to put on 1 kg live-weight gain.

Thus a 500 kg cow producing 5 litres of milk requires:

Maintenance	10 kg
Production	3·5
	13·5 kg good hay

If we wish to substitute say 5 kg of hay with kale or silage the rations would be:

(a)	8·5 kg hay	=	8·5 kg hay equivalent
	20 kg kale (4 × 5)	=	5·0 kg hay equivalent
			13·5 kg hay equivalent
(b)	8·5 kg hay	=	8·5 kg hay equivalent
	15 kg silage	=	5·0 kg hay equivalent
			13·5 kg hay equivalent

Perhaps you may wish to feed silage only, as with a self-feed silage system. In this case the 13·5 kg hay equivalent is multiplied by 3 – thus about 40 kg of silage would be fed per day.

Budgeting winter feed

The aim should be to produce at least maintenance and, if possible, the first 5 litres of milk from homegrown foods during the winter months. By adapting the hay equivalents system it is possible to budget the winter feed requirements by making a few simple calculations.

If we base the winter period at between six and seven months or say 200 days, then each tonne of food fed will be equal to 5 kg per day. Therefore, each 500 kg beast requiring 10 kg of hay or hay equivalent will need 2 tonnes for the winter.

If we add to this the production of 5 litres of milk, a further 3·5 × 200 days = 700 kg of hay equivalent will be required.

Winter feed requirements for a 500 kg beast for maintenance is, therefore:

2 tonnes of hay

or   1 tonne of hay *plus*
3 tonnes silage

or   1 tonne of hay fed throughout winter *plus*
2 tonnes of kale fed before Christmas *and*
1·5 tonnes silage fed after Christmas

or   1 tonne of hay *plus*
2 tonnes of kale fed before Christmas *and*
3 tonnes of mangolds fed after Christmas

or   6 tonnes of silage

If we take say the hay, silage and kale ration and have a forty-cow herd our total winter requirements will be:

```
40 cows × 1 tonne hay      = 40 tonnes
         2 tonnes kale     = 80 tonnes
         1·5 tonnes silage = 60 tonnes
```

This will mean that we need to grow:

Hectares	Crop	Tonnes per hectare	Total tonnes
8	Hay	5	40
2	Kale	40	80
4	Silage	15	60
14			

Fattening cattle

Calculating rations for growing stock and fattening cattle is worked out in exactly the same way as for lactating cows. Each animal will have a maintenance requirement and the production part will be the nutrients required per kilogram live-weight gain. These standards are given in tables 14 and 15. It should be remembered, however, that outlying animals kept in store condition will have a higher maintenance requirement than yarded stock receiving large amounts of concentrates for finishing. The old adage that a 'dry bed is worth an extra feed' is certainly true and every endeavour should be made to house cattle in comfortable, dry surroundings.

Table 14 Maintenance requirements of growing and fattening cattle

Live-weight (kg)	Maintenance energy requirements (kg SE per day)	Maintenance protein requirements (kg PE per day)
150	1·35	0·123
200	1·60	0·154
250	1·80	0·174
300	2·00	0·200
350	2·25	0·225
400	2·45	0·245
450	2.70	0·270
500	2·90	0·290
550	3·10	0·310
600	3·36	0·336
650	3·55	0·350
700	3·70	0·370

Table 15 Production standards for beef cattle

	Age	Kg SE per kg l.w. gain
Normal growth	Birth–3 months	1.25
	3 months–6 months	1·50
	6 months–12 months	2·00
	12 months–24 months	2·25
Fattening baby beeves:	Early stages	2·00
	Late stages	3·00
Fattening older cattle (3 years or more):	Early stages	2.25
	Middle stages	3·00
	Late stages	3·50–4.00

Example Ration for a 300 kg Charolais steer about 1 year old and fed to gain 1 kg live-weight per day. If we use best quality hay for maintenance and proprietary rearing cake for production, the calculations will be:

Maintenance	2·0 kg SE per day
Production gain 1 kg per day	2·25 kg SE per day
	4·25 kg SE per day

$$\text{Maintenance from hay} = \frac{35 \text{ SE}}{100} \times \frac{2 \cdot 0}{1} = 7 \text{ kg hay per day}$$

$$\text{Production from cake} = \frac{70}{100} \times \frac{2 \cdot 25}{1} = \text{Approx. } 1 \cdot 5 \text{ kg cake per day}$$

Example   Ration for a 550 kg Hereford × Friesian steer, 3 years old, gaining 1 kg per day, in the final stages of fattening. Fed on silage and fattening cake:

Maintenance   3·10 kg SE per day
Production gain 1 kg per day   <u>4·0</u> kg SE per day
                                 7·10

$$\text{Maintenance from silage} \quad \frac{12 \text{ SE}}{100} \times \frac{3 \cdot 10}{1} = 37 \text{ kg silage per day}$$

$$\text{Production from cake} \quad \frac{70}{100} \times \frac{4}{1} = 2 \cdot 8 \text{ kg cake per day}$$

These examples show quite clearly the extra food required by cattle in the final stages of fattening compared with the younger, growing animal. Although both animals are achieving the same live-weight gain the 3-year-old steer is consuming 7·10 kg SE per day compared with the yearling steer's 4·25 SE per day.

Summer feeding: grazing

Grass is a living plant, which is constantly changing in food value. It is very difficult to say with accuracy what the feeding value of a particular sward is likely to be, but we can generalize to some extent by stating that young leafy grass is high in protein, and that the feeding value drops markedly once grass approaches the flowering stage. This is due to the increased proportion of fibre, which makes the grass less digestible.

With beef cattle it is best to graze the grass when between 200 and 300 mm high. Grass grazed at 100 mm will be richer in protein than older grass, but this extra protein is not needed by the beef animal and may, in fact, be too laxative for cattle.

At the 200–300 mm stage, the grass will have sufficient fibre to prevent scouring. The only disadvantage is that there will be more wastage of grass with this form of management due to soiling.

To get the maximum production from grass, there must be some control over the grazing, either by using an electric fence or by dividing the pasture off into paddocks.

Chapter Sixteen
Traditional Fattening of Beef Cattle

''Tis the eye of the feeder that fattens the beast.'

The traditional way of finishing cattle is to purchase stores reared in the upland areas and to fatten them in the lowlands, either on the rich feeding pastures of the Midlands or in yards during the winter, a practice most common in the eastern counties.

Buying store cattle

Farmers look for strongly made, blocky cattle, that carry a high proportion of beef blood. Grassland feeders prefer the Hereford cross, whilst yard feeders look for the Angus or Beef Shorthorn cross.

Cattle dealers

Many farmers rely upon reputable cattle dealers to buy their stores. The dealer visits markets practically every day, and has the opportunity of inspecting a wide variety of stock. He is able to select the stock to suit the buyer's requirements. In this way, a farmer in East Anglia may telephone a dealer in Herefordshire asking for 'forty Hereford × Friesian yearling de-horned steers, about 400 kg at not more than so much per 100 kg'. Within a few days the dealer will purchase the cattle and send them either by rail or road to the new owner. Dealers charge a commission for their work and this varies from a few pence per head for stores up to £5 per head for suckler cows.

The market

If you prefer to spend your own money and inspect the cattle before purchase, then sooner or later you will visit a cattle auction.

Choose a cattle market that offers the necessary facilities for your purpose. Amongst these may be:

(a) Wide selection of cattle – at least 800–1000 stores in the catalogue. Some markets hold a two-day sale, selling steers one day and heifers the following day.
(b) Adequate loading arrangements which will allow quick despatch of cattle.
(c) If you intend to move your cattle by rail, ensure that there is a loading officer and that the market has suitable railway sidings and pens.
(d) Easy access to and from the market with car parks. Nothing is more annoying than to be held up in a traffic jam as you approach the market and find the car park full!

Buying cattle

When visiting a cattle auction for the first time, it is good sense to introduce yourself to the auctioneer before the sale commences. Auctioneers have remarkable memories for names and you will be pleasantly surprised when you make your purchase to hear the auctioneer say 'Sold to Mr —— from ——'.

Before the auction starts, inspect the lots of cattle that suit your needs. Value the stock and mark your catalogue at what you are prepared to pay per 50 kg. All cattle are weighed just before they enter the auction ring and their weight is chalked on a board. It is quite a simple matter for you to multiply the average weight by the price you are willing to pay per 50 kg.

Example:

LOT	75
No. of stock	10
Average weight	400 kg

Once you have 'fixed' a price per head for your intended purchase, it is best to stick firmly to your valuation. It is very easy to be persuaded by a good auctioneer ('Don't miss them for the sake of 50p, sir!') into spending more than you intend.

Date of purchase

Cattle prices vary according to supply and demand, quality of animal, and time of year. Cattle sold as stores in the winter will not cost as much as cattle sold in May.

If a farmer has some sheltered, free-draining, land, it would pay him to buy outwintered store cattle in late January to February and keep them 'lying out' on the sheltered field until the grazing season. It is often said that the difference between profit and loss in fattening cattle depends greatly on the buying and selling ability of the farmer.

Steers or heifers

The majority of farmers prefer to buy steers rather than heifers, and usually one has to pay a little more for steers. This is because steers are later to mature and will remain firm-fleshed (finished) for a longer period than heifers which tend to put on patches of fat once they mature. This is important when marketing fat cattle off grass, as frequently there is a glut of cattle in the early autumn and this leads to lower prices. The farmer with steers is able to keep his cattle until the market price improves, and he thus makes a higher profit.

If heifers are bought, they should be finished quickly and sold fat when 18–20 months old at around 400–450 kg.

Butchers dislike older heifers and will not pay as much for them. This is because the conformation changes with age, and a heifer approaching 3 years old will yield a similar carcass to that of a cow.

Grassland fattening

This is normally practised in districts where rich grazing pastures are found. The riverside pastures along the Trent, Severn, Avon and Wye are good examples. The special features of these fields are high water-table and winter flooding that keep reserves of moisture in the soil, and these encourage a steady growth of good quality grass throughout the summer.

The stocking rate must be carefully adjusted to the amount of grass available, for overstocking will lead to loss of condition, and perhaps the need to feed supplementary concentrates, while understocking will lead to a wastage of grass and nutrients. If the grass gets too far ahead of the cattle it will become stemmy, less digestible and consequently lower in feeding value. The very best pastures are usually reserved for well-made, strong-boned steers, and the second quality pastures left to be grazed by heifers and barren cows.

As a guide to stocking rates, one can usually reckon on two to three steers and perhaps a few ewes and lambs to the hectare.

A pasture should be divided into four or five paddocks, either with an electric fence or some more permanent division. This allows rotational grazing to be practised, and, should there be a surplus of grass, one of the paddocks might be cut for hay or silage.

Under favourable conditions, cattle may be expected to put on nearly 1 kg a day or 25 kg a month, which means that in the normal grazing season cattle may increase in live-weight by 150 kg or more. Some farmers aim to fatten cattle out by late August or September and then to buy in store lambs to feed out before winter. This suits riverside meadows which tend to lie wet, for sheep will not poach the sward as much as will cattle.

Concentrate feeding

Recently, farmers have adapted methods of intensively stocking cattle on heavily fertilized pastures in an attempt to increase profits. One of the snags is that the rich, high protein grass makes the cattle scour, rather than fatten. This has been overcome by feeding 1–2 kg per head of high energy, low protein concentrate such as rolled barley or maize cubes. The extra carbohydrates balance the excess protein from the grass and so make a more suitable diet.

Cattle may be stocked at up to five steers per hectare with this system, which is well suited to producing light-weight, grass-fattened cattle.

Yard feeding

Yard feeding has always been considered an art, rather than a science. Beef cattle have often been yard fed solely for the purpose of making farmyard manure or to consume cheap arable by-products. Often such enterprises have been unprofitable, the only justification being that the farmer liked the job and was proud to show his fat animals to visiting friends and neighbours.

General management

Today we must adopt methods of food and weight recording and feed balanced rations while maintaining high standards of stock-manship if we are to stay in business.

A cattle weighbridge should be considered an essential piece of equipment for the serious cattle feeder. The Agricultural Development and Advisory Service (ADAS) and most national foodstuff manufacturers will analyse your samples of homegrown foods, usually free of charge. In addition, advice will be offered on formulating and balancing suitable rations according to the animals' needs.

To illustrate the general management of feeding cattle, let us assume that 400–450 kg stores have been purchased with the aim of feeding them out at around 500–550 kg in approximately four months.

On arrival, the cattle should be immediately housed in well-strawed, airy yards, free from draughts and driving rain. For the first few days, the hay racks should be kept full with leafy, good quality hay. A clean water supply must be available and the cattle left undisturbed to allow them to settle down.

It is well worth while after this 'settling period', to run the cattle over a weigh scales/cattle crush, checking the weight of each beast and noting its ear tag number. At the same time you may dust the animals' backs freely with lice powder as a preventative treatment, and dose each animal with a roundworm anthelmintic drench, if· this is thought necessary.

If you know that the stock have been exposed to the warble-fly during the grazing season, then treat them with a systematic insecticide by pouring the recommended dose along each animal's spine.

Some farmers clip the hair off the backbone at this time, claiming that it prevents lice and helps to stop the cattle from sweating in the later fattening stage.

Following this treatment we now start to increase the quality of our rations so that the beasts gain 0·9–1 kg a day.

Rations

The rations will, of course, depend largely upon the particular homegrown foods available. On arable farms, the chief constituents will be straw and roots, whilst in the semi-arable areas, meadow hay and silage will play a greater part. Homegrown barley meal and rolled oats, supplemented with a little groundnut cake, will probably be the main concentrate food.

The hay equivalents system described in Chapter 15 may be used to compile suitable rations (see page 140). A few examples are given below and you may care to check the energy and protein content of each ration by referring to the tables and text in Chapter 15.

For example, a 400 kg steer may be fed for maintenance per day:

(a) 8 kg good quality hay

(b) 24 kg good quality silage

(c) 3 kg good quality hay
     20 kg kale

(d) 5 kg good quality hay
     21 kg swedes

The production ration is usually composed of a mixture of concentrates, fed at the rate of 3–4 kg per expected kg live-weight gain.

The amount of protein in the ration will depend largely upon the analysis of the maintenance ration. If large amounts of oat straw are used, then a high protein product ration will be necessary. On the other hand, if high quality silage is fed, no extra protein will be needed. Indeed, if the silage is of really high quality, it will be possible to feed the cattle for maintenance and production from silage alone.

Should the stock appear to be hungry after you have fed them, then offer some oat or barley straw in the racks last thing at night.

Order of feeding

Always feed the expensive foods first, and the cheapest last. Concentrates are the most expensive, hay is next and straw and roots cheapest. Obviously it is better to have straw wasted than concentrates. A suitable daily timetable when feeding hay, swedes and concentrates would be:

7 a.m.   Clean out troughs and racks if necessary. Check water
         supply. Feed half allowance of concentrates and 1–2 kg hay

9 a.m.   (after stockman's breakfast). Full allowance of clean,
         whole roots. Straw down yards and leave cattle
         undisturbed

4 p.m.   Feed half allowance of concentrates and 1–2 kg hay
5 p.m.   1 kg good quality oat or barley straw for cattle to pull
         at overnight if they feel hungry

Preparation of food

The old practice of slicing roots and chopping hay and straw is now largely discontinued, because of the high labour costs involved.

It is true that feeders of show cattle will boil grain, slice roots, feed treacle (molasses) with hay and give their animals a few raw eggs too! but this is certainly not sound economic business.

The main points to watch are that roots are clean, and undamaged by frost or bruising. Hay must be well-made, leafy and free from dust and mould. Concentrates must be freshly ground and stored in dry conditions. Oats are best rolled, barley may be rolled, bruised or boiled.

Points to watch when yard feeding

1. Allow adequate trough space – about 0·5 m per beast for 400–500 kg cattle.
2. Group the cattle so that all in a group are of much the same weight.
3. Stock should preferably be dehorned. Never mix horned cattle with polled, or bullying and hide damage will occur.
4. Bed the stock down daily, preferably with wheat straw. Allow about 5 kg straw per head per day or nearly 1 tonne per winter.
5. Allow 5–6 m² floor area per beast in covered yards.
6. Dose cattle for roundworms, and treat for lice and warbles when necessary.
7. Steers may be treated with hexoestrol 100 days before slaughter. See page 39.
8. Weigh cattle monthly.
9. Have homegrown food analysed for dry matter, starch equivalent and protein equivalent.
10. Feed a balanced ration, and remember to see that clean water is always freely available.

Chapter Seventeen
Intensive Fattening

Intensive beef production means rearing and finishing high quality, light-weight cattle that can be slaughtered when around 12 months old, or, with semi-intensive systems, a little later.

Intensive beef production has become increasingly popular since the 1960s, due, mainly, to the increased value of land prices and the subsequent increase in farm rents. It is not profitable currently (1976) to keep cattle for upwards of 3 years as used to be practised with traditional beef. Furthermore, heavy-weight steers are less popular with the butcher than light-weight cattle since they produce too much fat and a high proportion of 'low-priced joints'.

Therefore, it is young cattle that are popular because they cut a high proportion of 'expensive' joints and there is the minimum of wastage in the form of heavy bones, hide, fat, etc.

This young beef is extremely tender when cooked but it may lack the flavour of older beef.

From a farmer's point of view, intensive beef means a quick turnover of capital, better food utilization, and an opportunity to increase the size of his business without buying extra land.

The disadvantages are that good buildings are necessary; that a supply of the right type and quality of calves is sometimes difficult to obtain and that stockmanship of above average standard is essential if the enterprise is to be profitable.

Furthermore, it must be remembered that where large quantities of cereals are used, as for example in the barley beef system, the price of the calf and cereals and the sale price of the beast must be carefully studied. Frequently we have seen cheap cereals and expensive calves one year and a quick change to expensive cereals and cheaper calves by the next year. Also, the sale value will fluctuate according to supply and demand for the finished animal.

Barley beef

This system of intensive fattening beef cattle was first investigated by Dr T. R. Preston at the Rowatt Research Institute, Aberdeen. Preston published, in 1959, the results of feeding large quantities of rolled barley to Friesian steers. This system is now universally known as the barley beef system.

Management of cattle

Pure-bred Friesian bull calves are well suited to this system. They grow rapidly, convert food efficiently, are late to mature and produce well-fleshed carcasses covered with a thin layer of firm, white fat. The Friesian steer is capable of reaching 450–500 kg live-weight in 12 months, and will slaughter with a dressing percentage of 56–57 per cent.

Dairy Shorthorn, Red Poll, Lincoln Red, and South Devon bull calves are also suitable, but not as fast to grow as the Friesian.

Charolais × Ayrshire and Charolais × Jersey calves have been used with surprisingly good results; but one could not recommend pure-bred Jersey or Guernsey bull calves for this system.

Bull calves are much preferred to heifers, because they mature later and so are less prone to becoming over-fat. Heifers tend to mature at lighter weights than steers and produce patches of fat around the tail head. Producing surplus fat is uneconomical, since it takes two to three times as much carbohydrate to produce 1 kg of fat as it does to produce 1 kg of lean meat.

When a beast lays on excess fat, its food conversion will widen, and it may need up to 8 kg of concentrates per kg live-weight gain, whereas the normal food conversion is around 3–4 kg concentrates per kg live-weight gain.

Calf stage (from birth to weaning at 12 weeks)

Only well-made, healthy bull calves should be reared. The calves may be raised on any system that fits in with the farm, although the early weaning method will probably be found the cheapest and is certainly very popular at present.

It is not necessary to disbud the calves as they will be slaughtered before the horns are big enough to be harmful.

Bull beef

There is some difference in opinion as to whether the calves should be castrated or not. The operation always leads to a slight setback in growth, and the entire (the uncastrated animal) grows more quickly and produces a leaner carcass than the castrate. However, it must be remembered that young bulls approaching sexual maturity may become 'playful' and possibly dangerous to the stockman. There is also a risk of a darkening of the muscle in the carcass and the possibility of an undesirable taint in the meat.

The steer, on the other hand, is docile, and will grow almost as quickly as a bull if implanted with the synthetic hormones stilboestrol or hexoestrol (see page 39).

After weaning (3 months to 7 months)

When the calves are 3 months old and weigh around 100 kg, their diet should be gradually changed by reducing the hay to 1 kg daily and replacing rearing concentrates with a mixture of 85 per cent barley meal and 15 per cent protein-vitamin-mineral supplement. The barley is preferably rolled into flakes, as this preserves the fibrous matrix found in the husk.

The barley diet should be fed in self-feed hoppers so that the cattle have constant access. The calves will consume about 2 kg of meal per 100 kg live-weight; a 350 kg beast will thus eat 7 kg per day. Hay should be restricted to 1 kg per head per day throughout the rearing and fattening period, in order to encourage the stock to eat the maximum amount of concentrates.

If straw is used for bedding, the cattle will try to eat it, in order to gain more roughage. This is undesirable, as the straw will lower the animal's appetite, and so reduce the barley intake. The cattle should be made to walk round the pen while strawing takes place, as this will make them soil the bedding and so make it less appetizing.

Cattle always thrive better if kept in small lots, for then there is less risk of bullying and the younger calves have a better chance of getting to the food hopper. To get the best results, barley beeves should be kept in evenly matched lots and not more than twenty in each pen.

Cattle reared in this way may be expected to gain 0·75–1 kg live-weight per day, and will reach 200–250 kg by about 8 months.

250 kg to slaughter

From around 250 kg live-weight onwards, barley beeves will make spectacular live-weight gains. Over 1·5 kg live-weight gain is not uncommon, and as much as 1·75 kg has been recorded. The food intake will rise and the food conversion ratio needs careful study at this time. The cattle should be weighed monthly, in order to check the conversion rate. Once the ratio widens so as to make feeding costs equal to the sale price, then the beast should be slaughtered.

Hormone implantation

The food conversion ratio will be improved and the daily live-weight gain increased if steers are implanted with 60 mg of hexoestrol about 100 days before the animals are expected to be killed.

This operation is easily carried out when weighing the stock in a combined cattle crush/scales. The hexoestrol tablets are placed in the loose skin at the back of the ear, using a special instrument (see Chapter 3).

Bloat

One of the problems of intensive fattening with large amounts of barley meal, is the risk of 'bloat'. Bloat is caused by a mixture of gases accumulating in the first stomach or rumen. Normally, such gases escape through the natural process of belching, but under certain conditions the gases are formed rapidly, and consequently they inflate the abdomen. An appreciable swelling appears on the left-hand side, extending from the last rib to the hock bones. Affected cattle are therefore distended, appear uncomfortable, walk with difficulty, and are sometimes found lying down outstretched.

Treatment

With mild cases, the animal may be given a drench of 0·25 grams oil of turpentine, mixed in 0·5 litre of linseed oil. Walk the animal quietly away from the other stock and house it on its own.

With acute cases it will be necessary to puncture the rumen with a trocar and cannula, or pass a tube down the animal's oesophagus into the rumen, to release the gas.

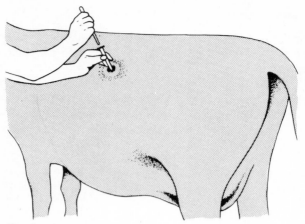

Fig. 39   Puncturing a blown animal with a trocar and cannula

It is very difficult to state exactly where an animal should be punctured, but generally it is in the middle of the inflated area.

The next time a veterinary surgeon visits your farm, ask him to point out the exact spot to you, and advise you how to implant the trocar and cannula in an emergency.

Chapter Eighteen
Semi-intensive Beef Production from Grassland: Eighteen Month System

The Grassland Research Institute, Harley, Berkshire, has successfully demonstrated an intensive system of producing light-weight beef animals off a mainly grass diet in 15–18 months. This system is known as Eighteen Month Beef.

Calves sired by beef bulls and out of dairy-type cows are used. This is because beef cross calves from dairy cows are in more plentiful supply and cost less than pure beef breeds.

The Hereford × Friesian is probably the best suited for this system because the inherited traits for easy fleshing off grass from the Hereford are combined with the rapid growth rate and leanness of the Friesian. Devon × Friesian also do extremely well on this system.

The Charolais cross is very popular but tends to produce a heavier beast and may require feeding until 20 months or perhaps two years to get a well-fleshed animal. Pure-bred Friesian steers are less resilient than Hereford cross under periods of stress and will take a longer time in the final fattening period.

Aberdeen Angus cross grow more slowly but mature earlier than the Hereford Cross.

The likely slaughter weights for different breeds when managed similarly will vary slightly but as a guide would be as follows:

Table 16 Slaughter weights and ages for various breeds and crosses

	Live-weight (kg)	Average age (months)
Charolais × Friesian steers South Devon × Friesian steers	500–550	17–19
Friesian steers	475–525	17–19

Lincoln Red × Friesian steers		
Sussex × Friesian steers	475–525	15–17
Devon × Friesian steers		
Hereford × Friesian steers	425–475	15–17
Hereford × Friesian heifers	400–450	16–18
Aberdeen Angus × Friesian steers	400–450	16–18
Hereford × Ayrshire steers	400–450	17–19
Aberdeen Angus × other dairy types	380–425	17–19

Adapted from MLC publication *Joint Beef Production Handbook No. 1*

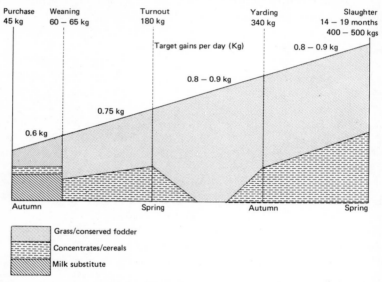

Fig. 40 Target weights and daily gains (Adapted from Meat and Livestock Commission

Within any group of animals, there will always be a variation in live-weight depending on the sex, health and genetic variation within the group.

General management (first winter to 6 months)

The usual practice is to buy strong, healthy Hereford × Friesian steers during the late summer to early autumn. This will enable the calves to grow steadily throughout their first winter and to reach a target weight of at least 180 kg by 'turnout' the following spring. The calves are usually reared on a 'bucket' system (see Chapter 8) but may, of course, be reared on a multiple suckling system where cows are available.

It is important that calves should reach 180 kg before turnout as at this size they are less likely to suffer from any setback due to weather condition or change in diet during their first few weeks grazing.

During the first winter either hay or silage may be fed in addition to a daily allowance of concentrates. Calves born in late October will require more concentrates per day than those born in August if they are to reach similar weights by the following spring.

Grazing management (6 to 12 months)

Calf rearing pastures should be rested over winter where practicable as this will help to reduce roundworm infestation and also promote better grazing the following spring.

Rested pastures will produce grazing one or two weeks earlier and this will help to save conserved food. On such land calves may be turned out from mid-April onwards, obviously depending upon the season and the farming district. In the southern counties 'turnout' may be earlier while in the north the first week of May is none too soon.

Continue to feed concentrates for a few weeks – rolled barley, or proprietary grazing nuts are ideal. A little hay may be offered although generally cattle are reluctant to eat this when they have free access to succulent grass.

The value of offering dry food is to assist the animals' digestion – very young grass has a high digestibility value (D value, see page 116) – and this will have a laxative effect on the calf. Feeding about 1 kg rolled barley and offering hay will help to prevent this. Ideally the grass should be grazed when between 125–200 mm high with a D value around 70.

Either permanent pasture or young leys may be used, but those with dense sward containing a high proportion of ryegrass will give the best results. Pastures with a high proportion of Timothy and Meadow Fescue will give similar live-weight gains per animal, but may not carry as many cattle per hectare as the ryegrass type.

The fertilizer treatment will depend very largely on the species of grass and the judgement of the farmer.

Ryegrass responds very well to high rates of nitrogen – up to 300 units per hectare. On the other hand, many cattle rearers will only apply basic slag to their pastures and rely upon clover to supply the nitrogen through the fixation of atmospheric nitrogen in the root nodules.

Whichever management is adopted it is important that the calves have plenty of fresh grass throughout the season. Rotational grazing using an electric fence to form paddocks, mixed grazing with sheep, or set stocking may be used providing the system allows a continuous supply of grass at the right stage of growth. Clean water and shade are also very important.

Given these conditions one may expect live-weight gains of 0·75 kg or more per day or approximately 20–25 kg per month.

Parasites

The two main problems are lungworms and stomach worms. The former may safely be prevented by the use of an oral vaccine and the latter can largely be prevented by sensible management and routine dosing with an approved anthelmintic.

New leys should be free from parasites but where permanent pastures are used, calves are best kept apart from older animals and should be changed on to fields that have been used for hay or silage before mid-July.

Second winter (12–18 months)

As autumn approaches the feed value of grass declines and one must not be deceived by the 'autumn flush' of grass. Quite often one finds more grass in September than almost any other month of the year but, regrettably, its feeding value is much lower than in the spring and summer. At this time you should commence 'hand feeding', i.e. offering a little hay or clean barley straw and some concentrates in addition to the normal grazing. This will keep the cattle in a thriving condition and maintain the expected live-weight gain of nearly 1 kg per day.

By late October to early November, depending on the weather and soil conditions, the cattle should be housed and fed on full winter rations.

Either silage and concentrates or hay and concentrates may be used as the basis for winter feed. However, whatever the choice may be you must use good quality rations, high in energy and balanced for meat production. Chapter 15 details the formulation of suitable rations.

By early February and until May, the cattle may be drawn from for slaughter depending upon their degree of finish and live-weight.

References

Beef Production Handbook No. 1, R. D. Baker, J. B. Kilkenny, A. W. Spedding, Dr J. C. Taylor, Meat and Livestock Commission, 1971.

Beef production from grass/cereal systems, Meat and Livestock Commission, 1970.

Three Systems for Beef, NAAS, Ministry of Agriculture, Fisheries and Food, 1969.

Chapter Nineteen
Future Budgeting with Gross Margins

The *gross margin* system of budgeting the potential profit of farm enterprises is now generally accepted by most farmers and advisers. With this system you divide the total cost into two main groups, fixed costs and variable costs.

Fixed costs

Rent and rates
Permanent labour
Machinery depreciation
Fuel and oil
Telephone and insurance
Bank charges, auditors, etc.

Fixed costs are those which alter little from year to year and may be expressed as permanent costs. Regular labour and rent are good examples and unlikely to alter unless you drastically alter your farming.

Variable costs

Purchased feedingstuffs
Seeds and fertilizers
Livestock replacements
A.I.
Contract services
Baler twine

Variable costs, such as purchased feeds, etc., vary according to the type and number of animals you keep and the crops that you grow.

Gross margin

The gross margin of an enterprise is the total sales or *gross output* minus the variable costs. Once you know the gross margin of one enterprise, say producing suckler calves, you can compare this with other products such as growing barley or wheat.

Finally, if you wish to find your true farm profit or *net farm income*, you deduct your total fixed costs from the total gross margin.

You will now find several *pro formas* which are set out to illustrate the gross margin for various enterprises. No specific prices are given because these change quickly from year to year. However, current prices can always be obtained from the farming press or ADAS.

Table 17   Budgeting data for single suckled herds

	£	p
Cattle Output		
Sale of calf		
Cull cows		
Calf subsidy		
Beef cow subsidy		
Hill cow subsidy		
Winter keep supplement		
Less		
Purchased or replacement cows		
A.I. or bull depreciation		
Cattle output	£	
Variable Costs		
Hay		
Concentrates		
Grazing – seed and fertilizer		
Straw		
Miscellaneous		
	£	
GROSS MARGIN		
including forage costs per cow and calf per year	£	
GROSS MARGIN per forage hectare	£	

Budgets for single suckled herds

Upland herds

Extensive system
Spring calving
Usually pure-bred beef breeds
Good quality bull essential to sire quick growing calves
Labour: 1 man unit to 120 cows and calves (3 man days per cow)
Cows eligible for winter keep and hill cow subsidy
Calves sold in autumn at 200–250 kg

Lowland herds

Usually associated with large arable farms
Autumn calving
Cross-bred beef/dairy cows may be used with advantage of size
and milking ability (double suckling a possibility)
Cows eligible for beef cow subsidy
Calves usually sold at 250–300 kg

Table 18 Factors affecting output

	Upland herds	Lowland herds
Calving date	February/March	October/November
Calving rate	96%	96%
Calf mortality	4%	2%
Weight of weaned calf	200–250 kg	250–300 kg
Forage hectares per cow and calf	1 hectare*	0·6 hectare
Herd life of cow	6 years	6 years
Cow mortality	0·5%	0·5%
Hill cow subsidy and winter keep	£24·50	—
Beef cow subsidy	—	£11
Brucellosis (if eligible)	£5	£5
Calf subsidy (1975): steers	£8·50	£8·50
heifers	£6·50	£6·50
Winter rations (cow):		
hay or its equivalent	2 tonnes	2 tonnes
concentrates	—	250 kg
Winter rations (calf):		
hay	—	250 kg

* Inbye land or its equivalent of open hill.

Table 19   Budgeting data for winter fattening of spring-born single suckled beef calves

Assumption	Steers	Heifers
Weight of cattle when yarded	250 kg	220–250 kg
Expected daily live-weight gain	0·9 kg	0·75 kg
Winter feed:		
hay	750 kg	750 kg
concentrates	750 kg	600 kg
Fattening period	180 days	165 days
All calves certified for calf subsidy before purchase		
Weight of finished baby beeve	400–450 kg	300–350 kg

Steers			Heifers		
Cattle output	£	p		£	p
Fat beast — kg @ £— 100 kg			— kg @ £— 100 kg		
Less calf — kg @ £— 100 kg			— kg @ £— 100 kg		
Total					
Variable costs (including forage hectares)					
Concentrates 750 kg @ £—			600 kg @ £—		
Hay 0·2 forage hectares @ £—			0·2 forage hectares @ £—		
Miscellaneous			Miscellaneous		
Total					
Gross margin for six months					

Table 20   Budgeting data for barley beef

Gross output	£	p
500–550 kg steer		
Calf subsidy		
Deficiency payment		
Total		

Variable costs		
Birth to 12 weeks:		
20 kg milk replacement		
100 kg baby calf food		
3 months to 12 months:		
1·5 tonnes concentrates (85% barley,		
15% protein, vitamins, minerals)		
250 kg hay		
Bedding		
Veterinary and miscellaneous		
Total		

Gross margin		

Chapter Twenty
Health and Disease

To become a good stockman you must always be observant and try to develop an awareness of the animal's general well-being so that you can readily spot any change in the animal's behaviour which may lead to ill health.

To do this you should first become well acquainted with the outward signs of good health. Generally this means that cattle are content at all times. They should be alert, but not excited; the coat should be clean and glossy in appearance. Ideally there should be 'lick marks' on the sides. The eyes should be bright and not sunken, the nose or muzzle should be moist but not running. Breathing should be steady and regular for all similar size animals. By counting the chest movements you can check the respiration which is normally between 20 and 30 per minute. Finally, check that the dung and urine are normal and sweet smelling.

Once you are aware of normal behaviour you will quickly recognize the signs of ill health. Any animal that stands alone, is slow to move, perhaps with a 'tucked-up' appearance or an arched back, should be examined immediately. Study the breathing and compare the respiration rate with other nearby stock. Look for any discharge from the eyes, nostril, mouth, vulva or anus. Look out for any signs of lameness or an unsteady gait, shivering or trembling of the skin, excessive coughing or choking.

With lactating animals a sudden drop in the milk yield, clots or blood stains in the milk, or any swelling or inflammation of the udder should always be noticed. Also, remember to check that the dung and urine are normal and free from strong smells, excessive looseness or costive dung; blood-stained or evil-smelling urine are further signs that all is not well.

By constantly studying the animals in your charge you will quickly build up an instinctive habit of knowing that your stock are 'doing' (in good health) or that a beast is slightly 'off colour'.

Notifiable diseases

Anthrax, foot-and-mouth and tuberculosis are notifiable diseases.

It is the duty of all those who look after stock to be able to recognize the early signs of stock affected by one of the notifiable diseases and to report this to the local police, the Divisional Veterinary Officer of the Ministry of Agriculture, or a veterinary surgeon. In the last case, however, always discuss your suspicions over the telephone and thus avoid the general practitioner's coming into contact with the disease. The Ministry of Agriculture have a specialist veterinary service which will examine your stock and take the responsibility of diagnosing and dealing with a suspected or confirmed outbreak.

Anthrax

The first sign of anthrax is usually a sudden death. You may inspect your stock in the morning and find that all is well yet by the evening one is dead. If the infected animal is found alive it will show signs of considerable abdominal pain, groaning and grinding the teeth.

The disease is caused by *bacillus anthracis* which can live in the soil in the form of a spore for many years. Once picked up by an animal, however, it multiplies rapidly and invades the animal's blood stream. Dead animals may show blood discharge at the nostrils and anus.

Where a death from suspected anthrax has taken place you must not touch the carcass in any way. Contact the Divisional Veterinary Officer immediately who will arrange for a veterinary surgeon to take a blood sample for examination. If anthrax is confirmed the carcass will either be burnt on the spot or buried very deeply in the soil and covered with quicklime.

Foot-and-mouth disease

This is a highly infectious disease affecting cattle, sheep, pigs and goats. The disease is caused by a virus. In cattle, salivation or slobbering at the mouth with a characteristic smacking of the lips and lameness are usually the first signs of the disease. The animal shows a marked rise in temperature and is obviously in considerable pain. On careful examination vesicles or blebs are found inside the lips and on the tongue. Vesicles are usually found on top of the hooves and between the toes. Cows may also have these blisters on the teats.

Once the disease is suspected the Ministry of Agriculture will immediately isolate the farm and impose movement restrictions on livestock in that district. Should the disease be confirmed then all cattle, sheep, pigs and goats will be slaughtered on the affected farm. The animals will be valued by an auctioneer before slaughter and the farmer will receive compensation for his loss from the Government. The premises will be thoroughly cleansed, disinfected and rested for several weeks before restocking.

Although slaughtering all the stock may appear to be an extremely drastic measure, it is recognized by veterinary surgeons to be the most effective way of controlling the disease.

Tuberculosis

This disease is uncommon today since it is controlled by the Tuberculin Order 1964. Under this scheme bovine animals kept in the United Kingdom must be tuberculin tested at prescribed intervals, varying from one to three years. Occasionally an infected animal is found other than by routine testing either in a slaughterhouse where tuberculin infection may be found in the carcass or offals, or on the farm in lactating cows. Should you find a cow that produces a straw-like liquid or if the udder becomes progressively harder and the cow shows signs of respiratory distress, then contact the Ministry veterinary surgeon who will make an examination and take a tuberculin test. Should an animal react to the tuberculin test it will be valued then slaughtered and compensation paid to the owner.

Movement of Animals (Records) Order 1964

By law, every stockowner must keep an accurate and up-to-date record of the movement of all animals brought onto and taken off his farm (see page 170). This record must be available for inspection by officers of the local authority, Ministry of Agriculture, or the police at any reasonable time.

In this way animals can be traced after they have left a farm should an outbreak of disease occur.

Movement of Animals (Records) Order, 1964

Date of Movement	Particulars of each bovine animal moved to or moved from premises mentioned on front cover				Number of sheep goats, or pigs (specifying which)	Movements to premises mentioned on front cover	Movements from premises mentioned on front cover
	Breed	Age	Sex	Ear Mark or Ear Tag. No.		Premises from which moved (including) Market, Saleyard or Fair) *and/or* Name and Address of person from whom delivery was taken N.B. – Both of tnese particulars are to be entered if available	Premises to which moved (including) Market, Saleyard or Fair) *and/or* Name and Address of person taking delivery N.B. – Both of these particulars are to be entered if available

Brucellosis (contagious abortion, Bang's disease)

Brucellosis is a disease which can affect both cattle and humans. In cattle the disease causes a highly infectious form of abortion and in humans it causes a fever known as undulant fever or Malta fever.

Brucellosis is caused by a bacteria called *Brucella abortus*. In infected cattle the bacteria live in the uterus and udder. It can be passed readily from the lactating animal via its milk, or if it has aborted the infected foetus and afterbirth will carry the infection. Other means of transmitting the disease are by cattle drinking contaminated water, or eating contaminated food, licking the hindquarters of cows that have aborted, or by contact through the skin, eyes, and nostrils.

Abortions are caused by the bacteria infecting the womb and cutting off the supply of blood to the developing calf. Usually the disease affects cows during the fifth to the eighth month of pregnancy, with a peak at the seventh month.

Should an abortion take place, then the cow must be isolated immediately and the cleansing and foetus destroyed, preferably by burning. Calving pens must be thoroughly cleansed and disinfected.

Control

There are two main methods of control. You may either vaccinate against the disease or blood test the entire herd and dispose of any infected animals. You may, of course, blood test and vaccinate.

Vaccination

Probably the best method of control is to vaccinate all heifer calves with Strain 19 vaccine (S.19) when the calves are three to six months old. (See free calf vaccination service page 172.) S.19 vaccine is a weakened strain of the *Brucella abortus* and when injected into the calf will cause the animal to produce its own antibodies, thus setting up an immunity to the disease. It is claimed that this immunity will last for at least five pregnancies.

Strain 45–20 vaccine

This is a vaccine of dead *Brucella* germs which is only used in special circumstances. It is not allowed in Accredited Herds but may be used on non-accredited stock following an outbreak of abortion. Two doses are usually given with an interval of six weeks between them.

Brucellosis Incentive Scheme

The Government has organized a Brucellosis Incentive Scheme in an endeavour to eradicate the disease from the United Kingdom.

Under the scheme eligible herds are paid a premium (1975) of 0·8p per gallon for milk and £5 per head for beef cows. Beef herds in the scheme are blood tested annually to ensure that all the stock are free from infection.

The Government also offer a free calf vaccination service for heifer calves aged three to six months. Farmers who use this service must have all their heifers vaccinated and these will be ear-tagged with a special tag provided by the Ministry.

Fig. 41   Contagious Abortion Free Vaccination Service tag

Compulsory eradication

In certain areas of the country the Ministry have started total eradication of infected cattle. In this case all reactors and contacts are slaughtered and compensation paid to the farmer.

Details of both schemes are available from your Divisional Veterinary Officer, Ministry of Agriculture, or your local veterinary practitioner.

Chapter Twenty-one
Diseases of Calves and Young Stock

White scour in calves

This is a very contagious disease of young calves which usually occurs before the calf is three weeks old. The disease is caused by a bacteria known as *E. Coli*. There are many strains of *E. Coli*, all capable of causing this killer disease.

The first signs of ill health are that the calf is found 'pinched up', looking miserable and obviously running a high temperature. This is quickly followed by a white or yellowish coloured scour with a characteristic rancid smell. Sometimes the calves may dribble from the mouth, and in most cases they are reluctant to take food. Over the next few days there is progressive emaciation and weakness and unless treatment is given death follows rapidly. Should a calf be infected there is a real risk that the disease will quickly spread to neighbouring calves.

Cause

Although the disease is caused by a bacterium there are many predisposing factors which bring about the disease. The most important of these is failure to feed the calf colostrum (see page 75). Colostrum contains antibodies against the specific strain of *E. Coli* found on the farm where the calf's mother was kept before the calf was born. Should a cow be moved to another farm just prior to calving, then she will not produce the necessary antibodies in her colostrum. Another major cause is poor housing, especially during periods of cold or inclement weather. Calves must be kept comfortable, in warm, dry, airy conditions and if subjected to adverse housing – dirty, damp, draughty, cold – they will quickly succumb to infection.

Prevention

Obviously avoid all the predisposing causes listed above. House your calves in comfortable pens, preferably individually. It is well worth while to provide an infra-red ray lamp over the calf during its first week as this will keep the calf warm and dry and thus avoid chills.

Try to allow your calf to suckle the colostrum from its dam rather than feeding from a bucket. This will ensure that the calf receives uncontaminated food, fed at the correct temperature, for at least the first two or three days of its life.

Any calves bought in should be isolated from the main group for at least two weeks as a further prevention. They may also be injected with an anti-scour serum and vaccine by your veterinary surgeon.

Treatment

Should a calf show any signs of ill health, which might make you suspect white scour infection, then it should be immediately isolated and kept in a scrupulously clean, draught-proof pen with an infra-red ray lamp. You can make a calf rug with a thick hessian sack and cover its back and sides by tying under the neck and belly. Bed the pen with clean wheat straw.

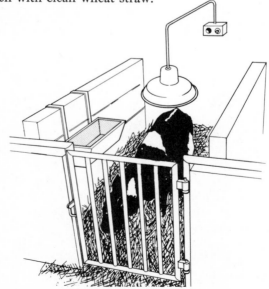

Fig. 42 Calf in isolation pen with infra-red ray lamp

Cease feeding milk or milk substitute and offer glucose water – dissolve a heaped tablespoonful of glucose in a litre of clean, tepid water. Offer the calf half a litre or more if he will take it of glucose water, fed at 39°C, three or four times per day.

If the calf is too weak to drink then gently and carefully drench it, but great care is needed to prevent the liquid from 'going the wrong way' and getting on the calf's lungs. This may well lead to pneumonia.

As the calf recovers you may gradually re-introduce whole milk or milk replacement with the glucose water.

In addition to good nursing on your behalf, your veterinary surgeon will provide a wide spectrum antibiotic injection which should control the strain of *E. Coli* found on your farm.

Salmonellosis infection

This is another highly contagious disease affecting calves, the onset of which is sudden and results often fatal. The disease is most likely to occur in late summer to early autumn and usually attacks calves between two and three weeks old. The chief signs are a high fever and blood-stained faeces. The bacteria causing the disease (*Salmonella dublin*) may be carried in adult cattle and 'bought-in' calves either by direct contact or through dung splashes. It should be noted that the bacteria can live in dung splashes on the walls of a calf pen for upwards of one year.

Where a calf is suspected of salmonellosis it should be isolated immediately and carefully nursed back to health. Veterinary assistance should be sought quickly. After treatment, thoroughly clean out the pens and wash the walls with hot water and a suitable detergent. Disinfect the pens and rest them before bringing in more calves.

When nursing infected calves take great care in your personal hygiene as *Salmonella* can infect humans causing the illness of food poisoning and typhoid.

Pneumonia

Pneumonia is the name given to diseases causing inflammation of the lungs. There are essentially two types: ordinary bacterial pneumonia and virus pheumonia.

The first case is usually associated with severe chilling or constant subjection to draughts. It may also be caused by careless drenching which allows liquid to lodge in the lungs or it may be a secondary infection following a serious illness like white scour or salmonellosis. This form of pneumonia, though proving fatal if not treated, is not infectious.

Virus pneumonia is infectious and frequently found during the winter months in groups of calves housed in badly ventilated buildings. There is much coughing and the calves rapidly lose condition.

The usual veterinary treatment for the bacterial type is injections of antibiotics. Treatment for the virus infected calf is more difficult. The vet may use antibiotics and a blood serum taken from calves that have recovered from the disease.

In both cases the need for good stockmanship and properly ventilated housing is most important.

Calf diphtheria

This disease attacks young calves, usually those under six weeks old, by affecting the mucous membrane of the mouth and throat.

If a calf appears distressed and uninterested in food, possibly with saliva running from its lips, then carefully open the mouth and inspect. The disease is characterized by greyish patches on the mucous membrance of the gums, tongue, cheek and throat. If a patch is carefully removed it will reveal the underlying tissues to be red and swollen and these are very painful to the calf when touched.

Infected calves should be isolated and then treated by the veterinary surgeon. As with all calf diseases the pens must be thoroughly cleansed and disinfected before housing further calves.

Black-leg

Black-leg (black-quarter or quarter ill) is an acute bacterial disease which can affect young cattle mainly between the ages of three months and two years. It is characterized by the presence of rapidly increasing swellings containing gas occurring usually in the region of the shoulder, neck and thighs. Death generally occurs within twenty-four hours but if symptoms are seen the animal will be very lame in one or more limbs with corresponding swellings which are very painful and if pressed crackle as if filled with screwed-up tissue paper.

The bacteria which causes the disease is *Clostridium Chauvoei* which lives in the soil and forms spores which can survive for long periods in the soil. Certain farms or districts are well known as being infected (black-leg lands). Most are either moorlands or poor quality areas often with marshy ground which favours the *Clostridium* bacteria.

Prevention

Vaccinate all calves at three months of age, before they are turned out to pasture and again at six months old.

Joint ill and navel ill

These are conditions found in young calves which may be caused by several different forms of infection.

Navel ill usually occurs in the first week of life and is caused by infection entering through the navel. This causes the navel area to become swollen and painful. The calf will run a temperature to around 40–41°C.

Joint ill is also caused by infection entering the calf's body via the navel. In acute cases death is rapid but in less acute cases the calf's joints – particularly the stifle, knees and hocks – are swollen.

The veterinary surgeon will administer drugs to combat blood poisoning and to reduce the swelling but, once, again, recovery will depend very largely on the care and attention of the stockman in nursing the calf back to health.

Prevention

On farms where these diseases are common, all calves should have their navel cords dressed with a strong antiseptic at birth. Iodine is widely used. Where calves are single suckled and, therefore, kept outdoors, it may well be worth while using a fly repellant ointment after the iodine.

Diseases commonly affecting adult stock

Hypomagnaesaemia (Grass tetany, Hereford disease)
This disease is caused by a deficiency of magnesium in the blood

and, while commonly affecting adult stock, may also affect calves.

Hypomagnaesaemia is most prevalent during periods of stress, such as in cold, wet weather or in the early weeks of lactation with suckling cows, and when keeping stock intensively on young leys, especially if large amounts of nitrogenous fertilizer are used.

Symptoms

In cows the symptoms resemble milk fever; the animal may be nervous and excited, then go into fits and finally a coma and rapid death follow. Young stock react in a similar manner. The disease may be acute or take a milder form, but in either case treatment is urgent.

Obviously ring for the vet, but, should he be delayed, you must make an immediate injection of magnesium boro-gluconate under the animal's skin (subcutaneously). Usually the dose is 400 cc for adult stock and *pro rata* according to size.

Try, if possible, to house the animal and cover it with rugs until fully recovered. Your veterinary surgeon will call and check that all is well, but in this case, delay in treatment may well mean death.

Hypocalcaemia (milk fever)

Milk fever occurs quite commonly in high yielding dairy cows especially those in their third and later lactations. In beef suckler herds the disease is less common but occasionally it is found with multiple suckling cows, mainly the high yielders. It is rare in heifers and second calvers. The disease is caused by a temporary deficiency of calcium.

Symptoms

The disease is generally found two or three days after calving but may occur during the last few days of pregnancy; during calving; or occasionally a few weeks after calving. The cow becomes excited, goes off her food, grinds her teeth and has a characteristic 'paddling' movement with her hind legs – first standing on one foot and then on the other.

In a very short space of time she will become drowsy and collapse. Her head will turn sideways in a 'swan-like' appearance.

If left untreated she will die either from milk fever or she will become 'blown' because she is unable to get rid of normal waste gases from the digestive tract.

Treatment

Make an injection of 400 cc calcium-boro-gluconate under the skin at the first signs of the disease. This will normally bring about a rapid recovery.

If the cow is unconscious then it may be necessary to give a small dose directly into the milk vein. This is easily found protruding under the belly. Great care must be exercised in making the injection as the solution is going directly to the heart. As a guide, after making the injection, allow a small quantity to drip into the vein and once the animal's body 'quivers' stop and complete the injection under the loose folds of the skin over the ribs.

Prop the cow up into a sitting position by placing straw bales under the shoulder and cover her with rugs or heavy sacks.

The vet should be called in even when the animal appears to make a satisfactory recovery as secondary complications, such as pneumonia, mastitis, etc. may set in.

The symptoms of milk fever and grassland staggers are so alike that you may have difficulty in diagnosing which disease is present. As a precaution you may purchase calcium-boro-gluconate with added magnesium, and similarly, magnesium-boro-gluconate with added calcium. This will give sufficient protection until your veterinary surgeon arrives.

Both solutions will be supplied by your vet and he will also advise you on how to carry out the treatment in an emergency.

Chapter Twenty-two
Parasites Affecting Cattle

Considerable losses occur in livestock through heavy infestation of parasites. A parasite is a living organism that depends upon a living host for its livelihood. In the case of cattle (host), there are two types of parasite that cause trouble:

1   Internal parasites, e.g. roundworms that may live in the lungs, stomach or intestines; flat worms that may live in the liver or intestines.
2   External parasites, e.g. lice, tick, blowfly, nasal fly, that live on the beast's skin.

Roundworms

There are about ten different strains of roundworm (nematodes) that are present in the stomach and intestines of cattle and providing they are kept in small numbers, they will do little damage to the host. It is only when the worm population rises to abnormal levels that suffering takes place. The most troublesome worms are *Haemonchus contortus* (twisted wireworm or barber's pole); *Trichostrongylus axei* and *T. vitrinus*, which cause black scour; *Ostertagia* (the brown stomach worm); *Cooperia*, or hairworms.

Roundworms vary in size from tiny thread-like structures about 5 mm long (lungworms) to over 300 mm stomach worms. They have separate sexes, male and female.

Life cycle

The worms mate, and the female lays fertilized eggs which pass out of the beast in the droppings. The egg changes into an immature worm called a larva. The larvae are extremely delicate on hatching and are susceptible to unfavourable weather. They like warm, moist conditions such as we find in the spring. The larvae become known as *infective* four to seven days from the egg stage and if picked up by cattle will develop into mature roundworms in about twenty-one days from the time the egg was laid.

If the larvae are not picked up immediately they will survive for several months and in some cases have been known to last for up to two years. Cow pats play an important part in larval survival, for although they may be dry and hard on the outside, inside they are soft and moist, thus making ideal conditions for the larvae's survival.

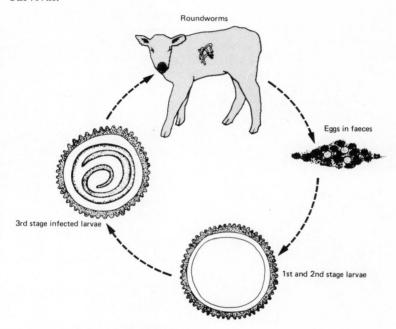

Roundworms

Eggs in faeces

3rd stage infected larvae

1st and 2nd stage larvae

Fig. 43   Life cycle of roundworm

Danger periods from roundworm infestation

The spring flush of grass occurring in late April, May and early June coincides with the turn-out period for calves and young cattle. This is the time when rapid increase in roundworm population – particularly *Haemonchus spp* – occurs. This worm, often referred to as the barber's pole, sucks blood, thus causing anaemia, loss of condition and, in severe cases, death. If left unchecked the spring rise will culminate in July and losses can be severe.

In early autumn the *Trichostrongylus* worms become predominant causing an evil-smelling black scour. In acute cases the animal rapidly loses condition.

Late summer is also the main danger period for lungworms causing husk. Also outbreaks of *Ostertagia* – the brown stomach worm – are likely to occur and continue into winter.

Control

The ideal way to control roundworms is by blending sound stockmanship with the use of modern safe and approved anthelmintics.

There is no doubt that well-fed stock properly managed are less susceptible to worm infestations than unfit stock.

Never mix young calves at turn-out with adult stock and try to keep the best grazing for the young cattle.

Mixed grazing with sheep, or grazing the sheep behind the cattle is sound, since, with only one or two exceptions, the larva that are infective for one species of animal are picked up and destroyed by the other.

Dosing programme

Dose all stock six to eight weeks after turn-out and certainly by not later than the first week of July. By this time the spring rise will be at its height and young cattle especially will be vulnerable to attack.

Dose again in early autumn prior to the autumn flush of grass and, where practicable, introduce dry feeding of hay or straw to reduce the animals' intake of 'wet' grass.

Should it not be possible to dose in the autumn, then drench all stock immediately they are housed for the winter.

Lungworms

Husk or hoose (parasitic bronchitis) is caused by the lungworm *Dictyocoulus viviparus* and is found widely in young cattle kept on pasture. The lungworm causes considerable damage to the lungs and bronchial tubes, which in turn creates discomfort for the calf, with considerable coughing.

The disease is most prevalent in damp, low-lying pastures.

Symptoms

The first signs of husk are coughing and irregular breathing. In severe cases the animal is most distressed and may have frequent bouts of coughing during which masses of worms and blood-stained discharge is expelled from the mouth. In chronic cases the coughing is less severe, but nevertheless, there is a rapid loss in body condition.

Because of its difficulty in breathing the calf tends to stand about in a distressed manner and takes little interest in grazing.

Life cycle

The adult lungworms live in the air passages of the lungs where they lay their eggs. These eggs are coughed up into the back of the throat and swallowed. They then pass through the digestive system and during this phase they hatch into immature larvae. Thus the infected animal will pass vast numbers of lungworm larvae onto the ground in its droppings.

The larvae now undergo a further change which, under favourable weather conditions, will take only five or six days. The larvae like moist, warm weather. In hot, dry or extremely cold conditions the change takes longer and many may die.

Having reached the *infective stage* on pasture, the lungworm larvae are able to cause the disease in any calves which pick them up when grazing. They pass down the gut and then bore through the walls to reach the blood vessels. Here they are carried in the blood to the heart and then to the lungs. Once in the lungs they do irreparable damage to the tissue as they bore through tiny air spaces and move towards the larger branches of the air passages. During this latter journey they are developing into the adult stage and are now capable of laying eggs and re-starting the life cycle.

Prevention and control

The most successful method of control involves providing calves with the immune mechanisms of the 'carrier' animal at the beginning of their first season at pasture, rather than at the end. This is achieved by vaccination. By this means, immunity to lungworms is conferred upon calves before their first natural experience of the parasite. Following field infection, such calves are likely to develop small but clinically insignificant lungworm populations, and so become converted rapidly from the artificially immunized to the true 'immune-carrier' state. Thus the highly susceptible phase in the calf's life, which has been exposed by increasingly artificial and intensive methods of management, is eliminated. In other respects, the natural host/parasite balance is not materially affected. Re-infection of pastures still occurs, and consequently the reinforcement of immunity from season to season continues. This method of control has proved highly successful, and is now standard practice in husk-endemic areas.

Lungworm vaccine is obtainable from the manufacturers by order from your veterinary surgeon.

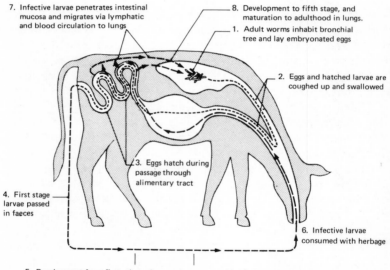

Fig. 44 Life cycle of lungworm

Platyhelminthes

The phylum Platyhelminthes consists of two main families that affect man and animals, namely the *gestoda* (tapeworms) and the *trematodes* (flukes).

Liver fluke

The liver fluke (*Fasciola hepatica*) is one of the most widely distributed and harmful parasites that can affect cattle, sheep, rabbits, deer and humans. It is usually associated with wet summers and in bad years can account for considerable losses in cattle and sheep. The earliest symptoms are loss of condition, the gums and eyelids become pale, and a soft, watery swelling may be seen under the jaw. A pot-bellied appearance follows, due to accumulation of fluid in the abdomen. Cattle get weaker, and losses can be very high.

A post-mortem examination shows the liver to be of a hard consistency. If the liver is cut open the flukes can easily be seen. The liver fluke is about 10–25 mm long and about 10 mm wide, the body being quite flat.

It should be remembered that cattle and sheep do not acquire any resistance to fluke infection and animals of all ages are at risk. Cattle and sheep must, therefore, both be dosed if there is a fluke problem on your farm.

Life cycle

In order to complete its life cycle, the liver fluke requires an alternate host to cattle; in this case the mud snail (*Limnaea truncatula*) is the other host.

The mud snail is sharp pointed, and rarely exceeds 5 mm in length. It is found in permanent and semi-permanent wet areas and does not usually frequent swift flowing streams, although the back waters often harbour small colonies of snails.

The essential phases of the life history are:

1 The adult fluke lays eggs in the bile duct, which pass down into the intestines and are removed from the sheep in the droppings. If the eggs fall on dry land, they quickly die, but if dropped in wet areas, they can remain alive for five to six months, or even more.

2 Between nine days and eight weeks, the egg hatches into a larva called a *miracidium*. This swims about vigorously and within a few hours is picked up by the snail.

3 The miracidium undergoes development inside the snail and after 6–7 weeks they produce new forms called *cercariae*. It is important to note that inside the mud snail a second reproduction

takes place, the miracidium producing about 1000 cercariae. The cercariae move from the snail and attach themselves to the herbage. Here the cercariae may remain alive for eight months or more.

4   The grazing sheep eats the grass with the encysted cercariae; the cercariae migrate to the liver via the blood stream and hatch into fully developed liver flukes. This again takes five to six weeks. After a further period of five to six weeks, they begin laying eggs. The process inside the beast is therefore approximately twelve weeks. Each adult fluke is capable of laying very large numbers of eggs; each egg is capable of developing into 1000 or more cercariae when in the snail; therefore one can easily visualize how serious this parasite can be if not strictly controlled.

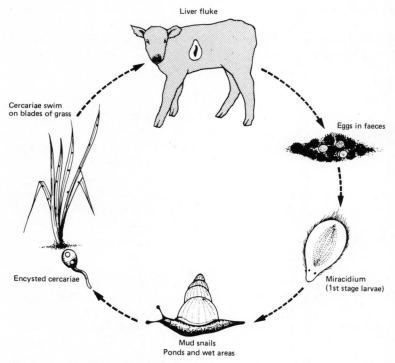

Fig. 45   Life cycle of liver fluke

The mud snail (Limmaea truncatula)

The mud snail hibernates during the winter months, but becomes active around March to April. The eggs that it produces give rise

186

to another generation which in turn reproduce a second generation by about July. A third generation is hatched in October. It has been found that a single mud snail in March will be the grandparent of 160 000 snails by October.

Prevention and control

1   The same fluke is harboured by cattle, sheep, deer and rabbits. Control measures must therefore be directed at all these forms of livestock when grazing together.

2   By killing the mud snails we can destroy the life cycle, i.e. by removing the alternate host. To destroy the snail spray all water meadows and wet areas in June or autumn with 2–3 kg copper sulphate in 200 litres water per hectare or mix 2–3 kg copper sulphate in 20 kg sand and broadcast by hand. You may also graze fields with ducks for they will consume the snails!

Treatment

Drench cattle and sheep with an approved Liver Fluke drench.

Approximate Conversion Tables –
Ready Reckoner

Weight

| kilogram to lb | | lb to kilogram | | kilogram to cwt | | cwt to kilogram | |
kg	lb	lb	kg	kg	cwt	cwt	kg
0·5 =	1·10			25 =	0·49	½ =	25·4
1 =	2·20	1 =	0·45	50 =	0·98	1 =	51
2 =	4·41	2 =	0·9	100 =	1·97	2 =	101
3 =	6·61	3 =	1·36	150 =	2·95	3 =	152
4 =	8·82	4 =	1·8	200 =	3·94	4 =	202
5 =	11·00	5 =	2·26	250 =	4·92	5 =	254
6 =	13·20	6 =	2·7	300 =	5·90	6 =	305
7 =	15·40	7 =	3·1	350 =	6·89	7 =	355
8 =	17·60	8 =	3·6	400 =	7·87	8 =	404
9 =	19·80	9 =	4·0	450 =	8·86	9 =	456
10 =	22·0	10 =	4·5	500 =	9·84	10 =	508

Area

| Hectares to acres | | | Acres to hectares | | |
ha		acres	acres		ha
0·5	=	1·24	½	=	0·2
1	=	2·47	1	=	0·4
2	=	4·94	2	=	0·8
3	=	7·41	3	=	1·2
4	=	9·88	4	=	1·6
5	=	12·36	5	=	2·0
10	=	24·71	10	=	4·0

Square metres to square feet			Square feet to square metres		
m²		ft²	ft²		m²
1	=	10·76	1	=	0·09
2	=	21·53	2	=	0·18
3	=	32·29	3	=	0·27
4	=	43·06	4	=	0·36
5	=	53·82	5	=	0·46
10	=	107·62	10	=	0·92

Capacity

Litres to gallons			Gallons to litres		
litre		gallon	gallon		litre
0·5	=	0·11	0·5	=	2·27
1	=	0·22	1	=	⁻4·55
2	=	0·44	2	=	9·09
3	=	0·66	3	=	13·64
4	=	0·88	4	=	18·18
5	=	1·10	5	=	22·73
10	=	2·20	10	=	45·46

Length

Millimetres to inches			Inches to millimetres		
mm		inch	inch		mm
25	=	0·99	1	=	25·4
50	=	1·97	2	=	50·8
100	=	3·94	3	=	76·2
200	=	7·87	4	=	102·0
300	=	11·80	5	=	127·0
400	=	15·70	6	=	152·0
500	=	19·70	12	=	305·0

Metres to yards			Yards to metres		
m		yard	yard		m
0·5	=	0·55	0·5	=	0·46
1	=	1·09	1	=	0·91
2	=	2·19	2	=	1·8
3	=	3·28	3	=	2·7
4	=	4·37	4	=	3·6
5	=	5·47	5	=	4·5
10	=	10·90	10	=	9·1

Glossary of Terms

Cattle

Bull	Entire male kept for breeding purposes
Bull calf	Either a male calf intended for breeding or a male calf not yet castrated
Steer or Bullock	Castrated male intended for slaughter
Cow	Female kept for breeding
Suckler cow	Female kept for breeding and rearing calf
Nurse cow	Used for multiple suckling, i.e. suckling successive batches of calves
Nursette	Machine used for rearing calves, which mixes and dispenses milk replacement powder and water in set amounts at constant temperatures
Heifer	Female reared either for breeding, milk production or beef
Veal calves	Calves slaughtered for meat when 2–3 weeks old
Bobby calves	Poor quality calves unfit for rearing, slaughtered at 2–3 days old and sold for manufacture,

	hence 'bobby' (few shillings in old currency)
Store cattle	Cattle reared for beef or breeding, that are neither gaining or losing weight – in store condition
Prime cattle	The very best beef animals – ready for slaughter
Show cattle	Cattle reared in such a way as to express their full potential for growth and conformation
Baby beef	Young animals, fed well, so that they may be slaughtered at around 12–15 months, weighing 350–400 kg

Terms used in beef production

Accredited	Blood-tested stock – free from brucellosis
Amino-acids	Chemical substances found in protein foods, e.g. Lysine
Anaesthetic	A chemical used by veterinary surgeons to produce insensibility in stock when performing surgical operations. Local anaesthetics are used for castration and disbudding
Anaemia	Illness caused by the lack of haemoglobin in the blood. Common in baby pigs, and may affect calves
Anaerobic	Usually refers to bacteria that live in the soil without the use of oxygen
Artery	A blood vessel that carries blood away from the heart to all parts of the body

Artificial Insemination, A.I.	A method of breeding used widely with cattle, pigs and to some extent sheep. Semen is collected from the male and inseminated into the female uterus with a glass tube or rubber catheter
Ash	The mineral matter of 'minerals' in feedingstuffs
Box fed	Usually refers to fattening show cattle in small pens, or 'loose box'
Breech presentation	Refers to calf presented backwards at birth
Brisket	Poor quality joint of meat found in fore quarter
'Bucket' rearing	Rearing calves on milk replacement powder and water instead of whole milk
Castration	Removal of testicles by surgery, or by crushing the spermatic cord with a bloodless instrument
Condition	Indicates the degree of finish or fatness in an animal
Colostrum	The first milk produced by cow after calving – rich in vitamins, contains extra solids and has a laxative effect on calf
Contemporary comparison	The method of evaluating an animal by the comparison of its own performance against contemporaries, i.e. animals under the same conditions at the same time
Dam	The maternal parent
Dandy brush	Strong, stiff bristled brush for grooming cattle

Dehorning	Removal of horns from growing and adult cattle; operation must be performed by a veterinary surgeon
Disbudding	Cauterization of the area around the horn buds, performed on calves when 3–4 weeks old.
D.l.w.g.	Daily live-weight gain
Dry stock	Cow not in milk
Ear mark	A distinctive mark, either tattoo or hole punch used to identify cattle or that calves have received a subsidy
Ear tag	A metal, plastic or nylon tag used positively to identify individual cattle
Embryo	The unborn animal
Gestation	Pregnancy – from conception to birth
Gestation period	Horse 11 months Cow 9 months Sheep 5 months Pig 4 months
Hormone	Chemical substance that stimulates body organs to work
Lot	A parcel of wool, pen of lambs, 'bunch' of cattle, litter of pigs, catalogued for sale by auction
Maturity	Full development of bone, muscle and fat
Muscle	Lean meat
Rig	Male with one testicle
Scour	Diarrhoea

Scrotum	Purse or bag containing the testicles of a male animal
Semen	A suspension of sperms held in the secretion from accessory glands
Sire	Male animal – paternal parent
Sound – Soundness	Healthy animals suitable for breeding or meat production – free from serious faults
Spaying	Surgical removal of the ovaries from a female
Starch equivalent	Measurement of energy in foodstuffs
Steaming up	Feeding supplementary concentrates during the later stages of pregnancy
Sterility	The inability to reproduce offspring
Stilboestrol	Hormone found in the female – synthetic stilboestrol may be implanted into steers to improve growth rate
Synthetic	Artificial production of chemical to produce a substance, e.g. synthetic oestrogens – hexoestrol and stilboestrol
Testicles	Sperm-producing glands. Normally the male has two testicles suspended in the scrotum

Selected Bibliography

BUCKETT, M., *Introduction to livestock husbandry*, Oxford, Pergamon Press (1965).

BRITISH VETERINARY ASSOCIATION, *Handbook on Meat Inspection*, London, British Veterinary Association (1965).

COLE, H., *Introduction to livestock production, including dairy and poultry* (2nd ed.), San Francisco, W. H. Freeman & Co. (1966).

DODSWORTH, T. L., *Beef Production*, Oxford, Pergamon Press (1972).

HAMMOND, J., *Progress in the physiology of farm animals*, London, Butterworths (vol. 1, 1954; vol. 2, 1955; vol. 3, 1959).

IMPERIAL CHEMICAL INDUSTRIES LTD and DARLINGTON AND STOCKTON TIMES, *New horizons of beef and sheep*, London, ICI (1966).

JENNINGS, J., *Feeding, digestion and assimilation in farm animals*, Oxford, Pergamon Press (1965).

JONES, E., *'Just your meat' or the judging of meat animals* (2nd ed.), London, Headley Bros Ltd (1955).

LAWRIE, R., *Meat science*, Oxford, Pergamon Press (1966).

LINE, E., *The science of meat and biology of food animals* (2 vols), London, Meat Trades Journal (1932).

McMEEKAN, C. P., *The principles of animal production* (2nd ed.), London, Whitcombe & Tombs Ltd (1943).

MARSHALL, F. H. and HALMAN, E. T., *The physiology of farm animals* (4th ed.), Cambridge University Press (1948).

PARK, R. D., *Animal Husbandry* (2nd ed.), London, OUP (1971).

STUBBS, D. R. and CATO, C. A., *Know your farm stock*, Aberdeen, Scottish Association YFC (n.d.).

THOMAS, D. G. M. and DAVIES, W. I. J., *Animal husbandry* (2nd ed.), London, Cassell (1971).

TURNER, B., *Hereford Herd Breeders Sketch Book*, Hereford, HHBS (1970).

WILLIAMSON, G. and PAYNE, W. J. A., *Animal husbandry* (2nd ed.), London, Longmans (1965).

THOMAS, J. F. H., *The grazing animal*, London, Faber (1949).

HAMMOND, J., *Farm animals; their breeding, growth and inheritance* (3rd ed.), London, Edward Arnold (Publishers) Ltd (1960).

PAWSON, H. C., *Robert Bakewell; pioneer livestock breeder*, London, Crosby Lockwood (1957).

HAFEZ, E. S. E., *Reproduction in farm animals* (2nd ed.), Philadelphia, Lea & Febiger (1968).

HAMMOND, SIR JOHN, *Animal breeding*, London, Edward Arnold (1963).

MILK MARKETING BOARD, *Breeding 10,000,000 cattle*, Surrey, MMB (1959).

MINISTRY OF AGRICULTURE, *Rations for livestock*, R. E. Evans (15th ed.), London, HMSO (1960).

DEPARTMENT OF AGRICULTURE & FISHERIES FOR SCOTLAND, *The feeding of farm animals*, Edinburgh, HMSO (1966).

NELSON, R. H., *An introduction to feeding farm livestock*, Oxford, Pergamon Press (1964).

TYLER, C., *Animal nutrition* (2nd ed.), London, Chapman & Hall (1964).

HALNAN, E. T. and GARNER, F. H., *The principles and practice of feeding farm animals* (3rd ed.), London, Longmans (1946).

SHEEHY, E. J., *Animal nutrition*, London, MacMillan (1955).

HAGEDOORN, A. L., *Animal breeding* (6th ed.), London, Crosby Lockwood (1962).

BARRON, N., *The dairy farmer's veterinary book; a complete guide to the farm treatment and control of cow diseases*, Ipswich, Dairy Farmer (Books) Ltd (1970).

BARRON, N., *The pig farmer's veterinary book*, Ipswich, Dairy Farmer (1957).

MERICK VETERINARY MANUAL, *A handbook of diagnoses and therapy for the veterinarian* (2nd ed.), Rachway, NJ., USA, Merick & Co., Inc. (1961).

MILLER, W. C., *Veterinary dictionary* (8th ed.), London, A. & C. Black (1967).

PATERSON, J. D., *Good and healthy animals*, London, Hodder & Stoughton (1947).

VOYSEY, A., *Animal anatomy*, London, Evans Bros (1967).

TROW-SMITH, R., *A history of British livestock husbandry 1700–1900*, London, Routledge (1959).

BLAXTER, K. L., *The energy metabolism of ruminants*, London, Hutchinson (1962).

UNIVERSITY OF BRISTOL, Department of Economics (Agricultural Economics), *The Irish store cattle trade: an examination of the factors influencing exports to the UK*, Marion J. Slattery, Bristol (1966).

UNIVERSITY OF EXETER, Department of Agricultural Economics, *Cattle production in Devon and Cornwall in 1964–65*, Exeter (1966).

FOWLER, N., *Beef and dairying management and production*, London, Hutchinson (1968).

GARNER, F. H., *The Cattle of Britain*, London, Longmans (1944).

MILK MARKETING BOARD, *The Charolais report: the results of field trials in England and Wales to compare Charolais bulls with bulls of British breeds when crossed with dairy cows* (1966).

MORTIMER, R., *Mechanised livestock farming*, Ipswich, Farming Press (Books) (1964).

ROY, J. H. B., *The calf*, vols. 1 and 2 (3rd ed.), Kent, Newnes-Butterworth (1970).

YEATS, N. T. M., *Modern aspects of animal production*, London, Butterworths (1965).

YEATES, N. T. M. and SCHMIDT, P. J., *Beef Cattle Production (Australia)* Kent, Newnes-Butterworth (1975).

COLE, V. G., *Diseases of cattle*, Sydney, Grazcos Co-operative Ltd (1965).

THE TV VET, *The TV Vet Book for stock farmers*, Ipswich, Farming Press (Books) Ltd, *No. 1 : Recognition and treatment of common cattle ailments* (1964); *No. 2 : Calving the cow and care of the calf* (1965).

BOUTFLOUR, R., *The high yielding dairy cow*, London, Crosby Lockwood (1967).

WHEATON-SMITH, C., *Breeding better cows*, Ipswich, Dairy Farmer (Books) (1957).

NORDBY, J. E. and LATTIG, H. E., *Selecting, fitting and showing beef cattle* (5th ed.), Danville, Illinois, Interstate Printers and Publishers Inc. (1956).

MINISTRY OF AGRICULTURE, *Buildings for the single suckling herd*, London, HMSO (1966).

WILSON, J., *The evolution of British cattle and fashioning of breeds*, London, Vinton (1909).

BOWDEN, W. E., *Beef breeding, production and marketing*, London, Land Books (1962).

UNIVERSITY OF CAMBRIDGE, School of Agriculture (Farm Economics Branch), *Beef on the arable farm*, P. G. James and R. J. Gayton, Cambridge (1951).

ENSMINGER, M. E., *Beef cattle science* (2nd ed.), Danville, Illinois, Interstate Printers and Publishers Inc. (1955).

FRASER, A., *Beef cattle husbandry* (2nd ed. rev.), London, Crosby Lockwood (1959).

FRASER, A., DODWSORTH, T. L., BALL, C. and BROADBENT, P. J., *In Search of Beef*, London, Crosby Lockwood (1970).

MINISTRY OF AGRICULTURE, *Beef production*, London, HMSO (1959, 2nd ed. 1965).

COOPER, M. M., *Beef production*, London, Nelson (1953).

COOPER, M. M. and WILLIS, M. B., *Profitable Beef Production*, Ipswich, Farming Press (1972).

MACDONALD, M. A., *Beef cattle production* (series of lectures), New Zealand, Massey Agricultural College (1958).

NATIONAL FEDERATION OF YOUNG FARMERS CLUBS, *Beef cattle* (YFC booklet no. 34), Peter Buckler, London, Evans Bros (1963).

WILLIAMS, S. and EDGAR, C. D., *Planned beef production*, London, Crosby Lockwood (1966).

WILKINSON, J. M. and TAYLOR J. C., *Beef Production from Grassland,* Australia (1975).

RUSSELL, K. N., *The herdsman's book* (4th ed.), Ipswich, Dairy Farmer (Books) (1972).